discussion book

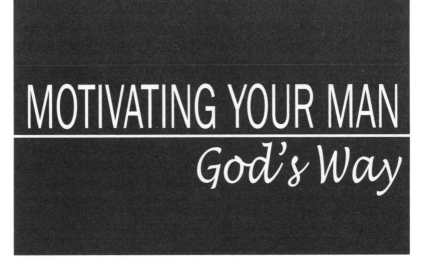

MOTIVATING YOUR MAN
God's Way

Applying One Word
That Energizes Your Husband To Love

Dr. Emerson & Sarah Eggerichs

Motivating Your Man God's Way: Applying One Word That Energizes Your Husband to Love

Copyright 2002 by Love and Respect Ministries Inc. All rights reserved.

Printed in the United States of America
Seventh Printing, December, 2008

International Standard Book No. 1-58473-084-6

For further information concerning Love and Respect Marriage Conferences, video, audio, and other resources contact us at www.loveandrespect.com

Cover photograph by Denis Boissavy / Getty Images.
Individuals in cover photograph are professional models.
Cover Design by Sun Designs with Art Direction by Dan Hyma

Edited by Eric Metaxas, Carolyn Kersten, Belinda Lund, and Laura Campbell

"Beyond Your Words of Love, Say It His Way" is a trademark of Love and Respect Ministries Inc. 2002

"Motivating Your Man God's Way" is a trademark of Love and Respect Ministries Inc. 2002

Visuals of Crazy Cycle and Energizing Cycle copyright 2002 by Emerson Eggerichs. All rights reserved.

Unless otherwise indicated, all Scripture is taken from the NEW AMERICAN STANDARD BIBLE ®, © Copyright 1960, 1962, 1963, 1968, 1971, 1972, 1973, 1975, 1977 by the Lockman Foundation. Used by permission. (www.Lockman.org)

Printing: Color House Graphics

Motivating Your Man God's Way (Part II)
Applying One Word That Energizes Him to Love!
Alone, With a Partner, or in a Group

Contents

Section I. From The Past, What Have You Done to Motivate Your Husband?

Section II. For the Future, What Can a Wife Do That Motivates Her Husband God's Way?

Contents, *continued*

Section I. From The Past, What Have You Done to Motivate Your Husband?

You have read book one: **Motivating Your Man God's Way: Discovering One Word that Energizes Him to Love**. That one word is respect. Peter in particular is clear: "Respectful behavior" can win a husband to God (1 Peter 3:1,2). This husband has not earned respect, nor does he deserve respect. But in Peter's mind, such respect is unconditional (1 Peter 2:18). His focus is not on your feelings of respect – you may not feel respect – but on your "respectful behavior." By implication, if your husband opens his heart to God, he'll open his heart to you. This is very exciting! Along with Peter, Paul summarizes marriage for you in a word: "respect" (Ephesians 5:33b). One word! This truth about unconditional respect is crystal clear, yet it has been neglected by the contemporary church. No one, to our knowledge, has taught on this with any depth even though it is half the equation for a successful marriage according to the New Testament (Ephesians 5:33)!

No where in the New Testament are you specifically commanded to "agape"-love your husband. God created you to agape-love in marriage. He won't command you to do what He designed you to do. Instead, God's attention is directed toward you applying respect. That is not natural for you, especially in conflict. Thus, it is the central teaching for you. Though both Paul and Peter begin with the word "submission" in their sections (Ephesians 5:22; 1 Peter 3:1), they conclude with "respect." In other words, the best way a wife submits is by putting on the attitude of respect. This is positive and doable. This takes the fear out of the word submission by bringing the apostle's primary meaning. To be a submissive wife is first and foremost to be a respectful wife.

Are you ready to apply what has been discovered? Let's get into the practical application. We believe your deepest desire is to "prove yourselves doers of the word, and not merely hearers who delude themselves" (James 1:22). We recommend going through the content with another woman friend (Titus 2:4) – or better yet, with a small group of women (Acts 16:13). We suggest reading the information for Session One, for example, beforehand and doing the assignment and then getting together to discuss your experiences. But use it as you see fit, breaking it up into whatever sized sections seem most manageable. We are excited about going into depth on this. Some of this you are already doing so these sessions will serve as a reminder (2 Peter 1:13), but other applications will be new. We believe you want to do in your marriage what the Bible positively instructs. We believe you want to become an expert on God's way of motivating your husband to be more loving. We believe you love God, have good will, and yearn to be a quality person. God bless you as you pursue this worthy course! It is simple. It takes work, but it works!

Session 1. Question: In a wife's view, what does it mean for her husband to be motivated? Answer: To be motivated to love her.

In our marriage, I want Emerson to be motivated to love me in the same ways that I seek to love him. And we believe you want the same from your husband. In fact, we believe you are reading these pages because that's what the title communicated to you – how to motivate him to love you more, and with feeling.

Countless times, women have said to us, "I have told my husband, 'I need you to love me. I don't always feel you love me.'" Wives want their husbands to love them in the ways they love their husbands; to feel, express, and respond to their love with feeling. To be the object of love means the world to a woman. She understands the Scripture, "His banner over me is love" (Solomon 2:4). Before marriage, a woman will say, "I just want somebody to love me." After marriage, she will wonder, "Does he love me as much as I love him?" A documentary on marriage in a primitive tribe revealed these sentiments. A wife was interviewed on what a wife looked for in a husband. The first words from her lips, as she sat on a mud floor in a straw hut was, "He is to love her."

> " . . . you do not love me . . . " – Judges 14:16

She asks him, "Do you love me?" He might rather bluntly reply, "Sure. I told you that 14 years ago, and if anything changes, I'll let you know!" Of course, he is missing the point entirely. A wife isn't asking her husband for information, but rather for reassurance. This is why a wife might ask, "Will you love me when I'm old and gray?" A wife will test a husband's love. To get back to our example from book one when a husband asks, "Where do you want to eat for our anniversary?" and she says "I don't know, you decide," what is really going on? It's simple. She is thinking, "If he loved me as much as I love him, he'd figure out where I want to go without me having to tell him." This is a test to reassure her of his love – so that she can be reassured that he feels about her as she feels about him.

> "How can you say, 'I love you,' when your heart is not with me?" – Judges 16:15

She knows she is motivated to love him but feels he is less motivated to love her. This troubles her. It feels hurtful and unfair. She wants to be special to him but feels he is distracted and focused on other things. She wants to be on his heart as he is on her heart. Burdened about this, she wants him to change and improve.

Reflection: What does it mean to you for your husband to be motivated to love you? What does that look like to you? What does it look like to you when your husband appears unmotivated to love you in meaningful ways?

Assignment: This week observe your feelings when your husband does something that feels unloving. If he says something in anger, makes an insensitive comment, does not listen to you when you are talking, or fails to do something for you, observe what you do in reaction. Try to get in tune with what is going on inside you. What are you expecting?

Discussion: Share with the group what it means to you for your husband to be motivated to love you. Share what is going on inside you when your husband comes across as less than motivated to love you in meaningful ways.

Session 2. Question: How does a wife seek to motivate her husband? Answer: Primarily by loving him, which begins and ends with talking.

> "Whom my soul loves"
> – Solomon 3:1
> "Tell me, O you whom my soul loves" – Solomon 1:7

God designed women to love. What female does not love to love? How we thank God that women love. Without their love, can you imagine what kind of world this would be? Where would we be without our mother's love? Perhaps the most common expression a woman speaks in the home is, "I love you." She says that when her children leave for school, when saying good-bye to a family member on the phone, or when writing a card to her husband. Listen to what women say. You'll hear the word "love" incessantly. Most women are expressive-responsive, and they express love and respond to love. This is their deepest value. They are so into love they can't imagine anything else.

Naturally, a wife is motivated by love. This energizes her. When her husband loves her in ways meaningful to her, it ignites her. In academics it has been called the sentimentality of a woman. When a husband does something that touches a wife, she becomes deeply sentimental. She will respond, "Oh, you're so sweet. I love you sooooo much!" The energy that floods the heart of a wife when loved in special ways is in-

> "My Beloved extended his hand through the opening, and my feelings were aroused for him."
> – Solomon 5:4

describable. When a man loves a woman, something in her responds to love, unlike anything else. She, in turn, gives, serves, cares, nurtures, and feels fond feelings of love when loved. She assumes her husband should too!

The assumption and assertion made by many wives is that a husband ought to be expressive and responsive to her love. As she seeks ways to love him, and as she seeks to be loved, she expects him to feel fond feelings of love for her. When she writes a love note to him, she wants him to feel sentimental feelings of love for her as she feels toward him when he writes her a note. She wants him to be like the hero in romantic novels. As a result of her love for

> ". . . When I found him whom my soul loves; I held on to him and would not let him go . . ." – Solomon 3:4

him, she wants him to be motivated to love her.

To a wife, one of the things that increases the feelings of love in the marriage is talking. When a husband talks to her in ways that are meaningful to her, her feelings of love can be ignited. She assumes that he should feel the same way. She wants to talk to him every day, not only so she'll feel love in the marriage but also so he'll feel love in the marriage. Talking should kindle his feelings of love for her. Talking should motivate him to feel love and to be a loving man.

> ". . . she pressed him daily with her words . . ."
> - Judges 16:16

Ask a thousand wives what is the key to a happy marriage and they'll say, "Communication!" Isn't this how he shows he cherishes her? In the view of wives, this is how two people emotionally connect. How can two people connect and experience love between them if they do not talk? She is energized to love with more feeling after good talks. This is why the wife is typically the one asking, "Can we talk?" Or, "We need to talk." To her, if there is good communication, the feelings of love will increase. She does not question this as the criteria for what creates love in a marriage. To her, if this results in her feeling fond feelings of love, it should do the same with her husband. If it does not, there is something seriously wrong with him and their marriage. If he is not motivated to talk, he is not motivated to love. That a husband is silent or wants to talk less than she does can be a serious threat to wives.

> "He . . . loves . . . and cherishes . . ." – Ephesians 5:28-29

Meaningful communication is made up of two things to her. One, talking about the positive feelings a husband and wife feel toward one another should increase the feelings of love. Talking positively about the relationship energizes a wife. She enjoys sharing with her husband why she loves him. She anticipates him telling her that he loves her, and why. Such talking reignites her feelings of love. When a wife says, "I love you," she wants to express her feelings of love, and she wants her husband to respond with such expressions. She seeks to energize him with her words, and she wants him to energize her with his words. There is more to the marriage than words, but words best capture her feelings. If her husband says, "I love you," she is tempted to ask, "Why? What about me do you love? Why were you attracted to me?" Her feelings are rekindled when hearing again that she is that special someone to him, that he treasures her above all others. This is why wives enjoy reviewing when they first met, and why her wedding pictures are so important. Few men show their buddies pictures of the tux.

Two, she wants to talk about the negative feelings in the marriage in order to clear the air and bring the relationship up to date, which also should increase the feelings of love. She wants to report the little daily marital problems on a regular basis. Talking about little problems on a daily basis prevents major marital problems. She wants to keep the relationship up to date. When the negativity is released, she is rekindled in her feelings of love. She assumes her husband should be remotivated as well. To her, when it comes to the problems there is a process: ventilate, express sorrow, seek forgiveness, reconcile, and experience rekindled love. When this process is complete, she feels wonderful about the marriage. She feels motivated. She thinks that he should feel the same way, too. She wonders, though, why she has to be the one initiating the deeper conversations about the two of them.

Reflection: How do you seek to motivate your husband? Do you agree that often you try to motivate him by getting him to talk? If he doesn't communicate as you expect, do you keep trying to talk to him?

Assignment: This week if there is a conflict, we want you to remain verbally quiet. We are not kidding. See if you can go quiet and remain quiet. We want you to enter the Scriptural call and discipline of quietness. Scripture teaches this as a way of winning a husband. He can be "won without a word by...respectful behavior" (1 Peter 3:1,2), and, "...the imperishable quality of a...quiet spirit" (1 Peter 3:4). This is central to your empowerment as a wife. This is not sexist teaching. Just as a husband needs to learn to live with his wife in an understanding way, which touches her spirit (1 Peter 3:7), you need to learn the discipline of quietness, which opens his heart. Peter said, "in the same way" referring to what he had just said about Jesus: "While being reviled, He did not revile in return; while suffering, He uttered no threats, but kept entrusting Himself to Him who judges righteously (1 Peter 2:23). A wife is called to imitate Jesus. Some wives have never been challenged to do this. Yes, we know you are convinced the conflict can only be resolved by talking. For now, do not view the goal to be resolution. The goal is to experience the discipline of silence. See if you can do it.

Discussion: If a husband wants to talk less does this mean he loves less?

Discuss what you felt about being quiet in a dignified manner – without contemptuous stares – on the heels of a conflict. Share what dignified quietness looks like to you.

Discuss the belief of women that unless two people talk, things cannot be resolved, even though Peter indicates a husband can be won without a word. How can that be? Which way will you go?

Has your husband ever said, "Drop it. Forget about it. Let's move on"? Many husbands are sincere, yet many women feel if something is not discussed, it is unresolved. To her, it must be talked about until she feels things are okay. What is the danger of this?

Session 3. Question: **Does a wife's way of motivating her husband work?** Answer: Less than she expects.

Generally speaking, a husband will be less expressive and responsive at an intimate level pertaining to love. Sociologists describe most women as expressive-responsive. This is rooted in their nurturing abilities. Wives get more facial wrinkles because they smile more in response to people.

> "But we proved to be gentle among you, as a nursing mother tenderly cares for her own children."
> – 1 Thessalonians 2:7

Their skin is stretched. They are more verbally expressive. Wives exclaim to their husbands, "Can we talk? The key to our marriage is communication! Why don't you talk to me?"

A husband is more compartmentalized. He puts his emotions in various compartments. He can poker-face it. One wife said, "My husband is a mysterious island. I am forever paddling around, but he does not permit me to land." So when she tries to get him to talk in order to connect and increase the feelings of love between them, she can feel more frustrated by what appears to be his lack of expressiveness and responsiveness at an intimate level. She feels she is always there for him when it comes to his desire to connect emotionally but is he there for her? Why won't he answer her?

> "I opened to my beloved, But my beloved had turned away and had gone! My heart went out to him as he spoke. I searched for him but I did not find him; I called him but he did not answer me." – Solomon 5:6

In the regular feature of His and Hers in the magazine *Marriage Partnership*, the title read, "Crybaby Loves Pokerface." The editors said, "For crying out loud, how come guys rarely shed tears during the most tear jerking of movies, while women have been known to tear up over a really good Hallmark commercial? It isn't because men don't experience the same emotional responses, says a recent study conducted at Vanderbilt University. Psychologists there monitored internal and facial responses of men and women watching emotion-tugging clips

> ". . . and standing behind Him at His feet, weeping, she began to wet His feet with her tears, and kept wiping them with the hair of her head, and kissing His feet and anointing them with the perfume." – Luke 7:38

from various movies. Men and women showed equal responses internally, but the feelings didn't show up on the men's faces." (Marriage Partnership Fall 1999).

Research shows that 85% of those who stonewall, who go silent when marital tension surges, are the husbands (*Why Marriages Succeed or Fail*, p. 147). Men are less expressive-responsive. Of course, that means 15% of the wives stonewall. So, no, it is not always the case. However, we believe those women who stonewall do so not because they want to but because there has been a breakdown in communication! Women want to talk about matters of the heart. All women have an intimate friend with whom they share the secret and intimate details of their lives. They do not feel obligated to do this; they yearn to do this. When first married, they felt their husbands would be their intimate friends. Yet, he was less expressive at that level. So she talked more and more. Scripture reveals that she can talk too much. This can turn a man off. This is why Peter is explicit: "your own husbands...may be won without a word."

> ". . . remain quiet."
> – 1Timothy 2:12

For those husbands who always talk, the subject matter is not about her intimate feelings. He is not engaged verbally about her deeper concerns. She eventually gives up and becomes quiet. Most women, though, keep pursuing and engaging their husbands on the emotional level. She keeps giving the daily report to build rapport. She follows him around the house when he comes home, but he tends not to focus on her as she wishes. She releases her emotions, hoping he will do the same. She talks to realize her feelings, but he tends to drift. She feels the love between them is less than it ought to be. Their communication is not what it ought to be. In fact, whereas a wife feels one must talk daily about the problems in the marriage in order to prevent major marital problems, a husband can feel daily talking about marital problems indicates there is a major marital problem! Whereas her impression is the marriage is up to date after such venting, his impression is the marriage is negative and not enjoyable. As one husband who conducts marriage conferences with his wife exclaimed one day, "Can't we just have one day when everything is okay?" Whereas she sees him as her burden-bearer, he feels weighed down by the burdens, or worse, that he is her burden.

Reflection: Could something other than you talking to your husband motivate your husband to talk to you? Could a shoulder-to-shoulder friendship with your husband energize him to talk? Do you want the two of you to be energized by the marriage or just yourself? If you want your husband to be energized, might he be invigorated by your mere presence? Might he be profoundly encouraged by you watching him do some activity, like you did during courtship? What if he was energized by a shoulder-to-shoulder activity without face-to-face talking; would you do this more regularly?

Assignment: When he comes home don't give your report of the day. Don't expect him to give his report of the day. Though in your view rapport is derived through the report, don't do any reporting. Do something with him shoulder-to-shoulder without talking. Watch the news with him, watch him play with the kids, watch him work on a project. Drop what you are doing for 20 or 30 minutes, and come alongside him without talking. If he asks, "What are you doing?" say, "I just wanted to be with you." Don't be upset by his teasing, "Well, what do you want, more money?" Most men will make some comment like that. Counter, "No, I was thinking of you and just wanted to be with you. Keep doing what you're doing, I like watching."

Discussion: Report to the group how your husband responded to the shoulder-to-shoulder activity without you talking.

Discuss the possibility that your husband might be motivated by your mere presence without you talking. Could his love for you increase without you talking? Is that impossible?

Discuss the objection a wife can make, "I don't have time for this shoulder-to-shoulder stuff." If she does not have time for this, does she have time to talk? Can a wife feel her needs are more important than her husband's? What does equality mean?

Session 4. Question: When a wife's way of motivating her husband isn't working, what does she tend to do? Answer: Most wives move toward him to talk even more, demanding that they talk.

When a wife feels love decreasing, she can be aggressive. When it comes to matters of intimacy in the home, a wife can be very assertive. She moves toward him, saying, "Talk to me." Imagine a photograph of a husband and wife that gets torn in two. A wife will do everything she can to tape it together, to reconnect the two people. In her mind, the best way to do this is by talking. If, though, the husband doesn't respond like she hoped, and doesn't express himself as she expects, she will become more assertive: "Talk to me! Now!" This is not true for all women, but most all want to talk. Some wives won't talk until they feel it's safe, and in tune with their feelings.

> "I sought him Whom my soul loves; I sought him but did not find him."
> – Solomon 3:1
> ". . . 'I must seek him whom my soul loves.' I sought him but did not find him." – Solomon 3:2
> "If you find my beloved, As to what you will tell him: For I am lovesick." –
> Solomon 5:8

At those moments, it is natural for her to be verbal and even critical. She tends to vent her negative feelings. Her goal is to increase the feelings of love between them. For that to happen, the two of them must resolve the issues and reconcile. She wants to express her hurts and frustrations, and wants him to do the same, very sensitively of course. She wants to say, "I'm sorry," and wants him to say the same. However, as she vocalizes about that which is upsetting her, she can overstate things. "You never! You always!" At that instant, he gets angry and withdraws, which frustrates her to no end. She thinks, "He must not be getting it." Or, she feels he is beginning to block her out and dismiss her and one more emotional tirade. A wife can become more expressive, more critical, and more negative. She can become, as one wife said, "venomous" when her deeper need for love is threatened.

> "It is better to live in a corner of the roof Than in a house shared with a contentious woman."
> – Proverbs 25:24
> "But he said to her, 'You speak as one of the foolish women speaks. . . .'"
> – Job 2:10

Reflection: When you feel your way of motivating your husband isn't working, what do you tend to do? Do you move toward him to talk even more, demanding that the two of you talk? Do you come across as controlling– barking a command? How does your husband view "the talk?" Does he decode your deeper cry or feel scolded? Whereas you feel love will increase as a result of "the talk," might your husband feel he loses your respect during "the talk?" How easy is it to complain, criticize, and be negative, expecting him to understand and talk?

Assignment: Instead of saying, "Talk to me right now," ask a question. Ask the question as respectfully as you can. "When would be a good time this evening to talk? Are you free after dinner? I'd like to have pie and ice cream, away from the kids so we can talk for twenty minutes. I am feeling burdened and need your listening ear. I feel so much better after I talk to you."

Discussion: Discuss how your husband responded when you approached it as we requested. If you did not approach him this way, is there resistance to anything that appears to honor him? Share how you typically approach him. Does your approach touch his spirit?

Some wives claim their husbands are wonderful, understanding and listen, even though as women they are negative and demanding. Is there any risk for a wife to continue on this course?

What if a wife is respectful in making a request to talk but her husband does not respond? Should she become disrespectful? Should she conclude this doesn't work with her husband? Should she conclude God's Word does not apply to her?

Session 5. Question: Is there potential for a husband and wife to enter a painful pattern?
Answer: Yes, a cycle of criticism and withdrawal.

As the couple sat across from the pastor and his wife, the other woman launched into a description of why she was unhappy. This complaint was made in front of her husband. She didn't have what other couples had. "I watch other couples. Other husbands look at their wives and talk. The husbands love their wives. I feel deprived. He doesn't look at me and talk. He does not meet my need for love. What is wrong with him? My marriage is miserable. He doesn't make me feel loved."

> "But she who shames him is as rottenness in his bones."
> – Proverbs 12:4

Complaint after complaint poured out of her mouth about her husband – in front of her husband! She was not angry. She was in earnest. But in her complaint about being unloved, she sent message after message that was quite negative. She was clueless about her belittling words. The pastor and his wife wanted to crawl under the table. This woman chastised her husband's core self and she didn't see it!

"Unless I complain he does not hear me!" Some wives know they are berating. From their view, how else will their husbands "get it" if they don't voice their complaints, criticisms and contempt? One wife acknowledged to her husband, "I should have verbalized my frustrations differently most of the time, but I saw only that you focused on my complaints better if I spoke harshly. Since talking to you rationally didn't help, I began talking irrationally. I do believe the things I said are true, I only regret trying to make points the way I did." This is female practicality. For some wives, if berating works best, do it. Samson's wife thought so. We read, "And it came about when she pressed him daily with her words and urged him, that his soul was annoyed to death" (Judges 16:16).

For some wives, this approach is justified. If the wife feels powerless and victimized, then there is no other way. What is amazing, many wives acknowledge the complaints, criticism, and contempt don't work. One wife told Emerson, "My crabbing and crying doesn't work." Yet, she had been doing just that for over twenty years. Her loving Abba Father revealed a different path, but she left that approach behind years earlier.

Wives need to awaken to something beyond their own feelings. If they don't, they undermine the very thing they seek. Husbands lose motivation to feel love and to act lovingly. A husband can shut down over innocent comparisons, inadvertent berating, and intentional chastisement. Just because a wife feels herself to be a loving person does not justify ignoring how her husband feels. Few men voice their deepest feelings. Instead, they emotionally close off.

A leading researcher of marriage, Professor John Gottman at the University of Washington studied 2000 couples over 20 years. He can predict within five minutes with 91% accuracy if a couple will divorce. In *Why Marriages Succeed or Fail*, he writes: "...men are far more likely than women to be stonewallers (85%) ...when tension builds...it often takes only the arrival of...criticism... (p. 147) ...Men avoid emotional conflicts by going off by themselves...If you ask a male stonewaller to describe his state of mind, he often says, 'I am trying not to react.' ...though his wife perceives his silence as an act of hostility (p.148) ... The wife is...likely to interpret his response as a rejection of her...she couldn't imagine needing to withdraw over such a minor criticism (p.151) ...Such interactions can produce a vicious cycle, especially in marriages with high levels of conflict. The more wives complain and criticize, the more husbands withdraw and stonewall; the more husbands withdraw and stonewall, the more wives complain and criticize. This cycle must be broken if...marriages are to avoid dissolution...if the wife becomes belligerent and contemptuous, the husband is likely to withdraw even more... (p.152)."

> "Thus says the Lord, "Stand by the ways and see and ask for the ancient paths, where the good way is, and walk in it; And you will find rest for your souls. But they said, 'We will not walk in it.'"
> - Jeremiah 6:16

Is this why God teaches wives to show unconditional respect? We believe the answer is an absolute yes! This command of God countermands her tendency to be disrespectful. She is trying to do the loving thing by getting him to be more loving. At a certain point, though, a husband does not hear her cry for love. Instead he feels she is sending a message of contempt for who he is as a man and a human being. Hear again the Word of God. God's word protects the wife from triggering the harmful pattern.

Ephesians 5:33 **Nevertheless let each individual among you also love his own wife even as himself; and let the wife see to it that she respect her husband.**

1 Peter 3:1, 2 **...even if any of them are disobedient to the word, they may be won without a word by the behavior of their wives, as they observe your... respectful behavior.**

Scripture teaches that if a wife does that which is unnatural – that is, goes quiet – it shouts to her husband! If she withdraws into respectful silence, seeking to do respectful things on the heels of his disobedience, God moves in. Many wives feel

> ". . . learn not to exceed what is written, . . ."
> - 1 Corinthians 4:6

though, that if they do not speak, nothing can happen. To these women, negative talking starts the reconciliation process; if she does not talk like this, love cannot be reestablished. She believes this because she has been silent in the past, and it did not work. While she was quiet, though, was she not a woman of dignity, displaying respectful attitudes and actions? And was she quiet for only a few minutes? Did she soon pour out all her negativity? Did things get crazy? Did he withdraw?

Reflection: Is there potential for you and your husband to enter a painful pattern of criticism and withdrawal? Are you the one who tends to criticize and your husband tends to withdraw? Or, are you the reverse? Are you aware of this cycle? How badly do you want to get off of it? Has God revealed that you have power as a woman to do that?

Assignment: Assuming you will have a minor point of tension with your husband this week, please evaluate what is happening inside your heart. For instance, if you criticize your husband and you observe him withdraw, what is your thought process? Do you perceive his distance as rudeness or even hostility? Do you interpret this silence as cold rejection? Are you baffled at his stonewalling in response to what you feel is a minor criticism? Where did it go from there? Did you lash out at him when he stonewalled you? Then what did he do? And, then, what did you do? Is there a cycle and habit of this in your marriage?

Discussion: Discuss with the group whether or not a husband is being childish as he pulls back from "minor criticisms?" Is it not okay for him to be overly sensitive to ongoing criticisms yet okay for you to be sensitive to comments about your body image and appearance? A wife tends to cry when hurt, but a husband does not cry. What does a husband do?

Do you feel you have a right and even a responsibility to get through to him when he stonewalls? Does the end (resolution of the conflict) justify the means (being belligerent and contemptuous)?

When you criticize your husband do you see this as potentially increasing the feelings of love between you? Does he see this as decreasing the feeling that you respect him, and thus he resists talking more and more?

Some of you have broken this cycle of criticism and withdrawal. Share some of the ways you are doing this.

Session 6. Question: Why do wives and husbands tend to experience common cycles?

Answer: Neither of them understand what the Bible reveals about the secret to cracking the communication between husbands and wives.

> "Enjoy life with the woman . . . you love . . ."
> - Ecclesiastes 9:9

A husband does not fully understand his wife's code. The code she sends in her criticism is, "I need to feel you love me," but he doesn't always decode it. If he did, his marriage would be so much more enjoyable! Unhappily, the more negative and critical she becomes in an effort to motivate him, the more he loses motivation to move toward her in love.

> ". . . I screamed."
> - Genesis 39:14
> ". . . I raised my voice and screamed,"
> - Genesis 39:15
> ". . . I raised my voice and screamed,"
> - Genesis 39:18

Dr. Gottman found that as a wife expresses her negative feelings and vents in a critical manner, a husband begins to feel that she has contempt for who he is as a man. It is obvious to her she is feeling unloved, and that is why she is negatively reacting. He should see underneath her disrespectful reactions to her cry for his love. However, none of his male friends would talk to him the way his wife does in the privacy of their home. In fact, if one man talked to another man the way a wife sometimes talks to her husband, those two men would get in a bloody fistfight and/or end the friendship. This is why a husband says, "Quit provoking me. You are just trying to pick a fight with me." She scratches her head in bewilderment. She feels some of her outbursts are normal. What woman does not scream or cry sometimes? Come on! She is trying to connect, not create conflict. Every wife knows that if he loved her in the face of her disrespect, she'd melt. That's why she is being disrespectful! If only he could see that her disrespect is expressed to motivate him to be more loving! If only he would discover the secret that cracks the communication code his wife is sending him! (In our Love and Respect Marriage Conference, we show husbands how to do this). However, on his own, that code is tough to crack! That is comparable to a husband reacting in very unloving ways to motivate his wife to be more respectful. Will the wife crack the code? That isn't easy. What wife is motivated to be respectful on the heels of her husband's harshness? So too, what husband is motivated to be a loving person on the heels of his wife's contempt?

Just the appearance of disrespect can knock the wind out of him! He reacts to it in a way that she feels is angry and arrogant, which convinces her even more that he has a problem. Think of King David again. Was this his or her problem? Michal, his wife, calls him a fool and David counters with strong words about his need to be esteemed. Is David arrogant or is this what happens in even a godly wise husband when he is verbally despised? "But when David returned to bless his household, Michal the daughter of Saul came out to meet David and said, 'How the king of Israel distinguished himself today! He uncovered himself today in the eyes of his servants' maids as one of the foolish ones shamelessly uncovers himself!' So David said to Michal, 'It was before the Lord, who chose me above your father and above all his house, to appoint me ruler over the people of the Lord, over Israel; therefore I will celebrate before the Lord. And I will be more lightly esteemed than this and will be humble in my own eyes'" (2 Samuel 6:20-22). We then read, "And Michal the daughter of Saul had no child to the day of her death" (2 Samuel 6:23).

Oh, that wives would understand the wisdom of Ephesians 5:33: "Nevertheless let each individual among you also love his own wife even as himself; and let the wife see to it that she respect her husband." Love is her deepest need. Respect is his deepest need. This is the secret that cracks the communication code!

Without love she reacts. She needs love like she needs air to breathe. When the elephant sits on her air hose, she will react. How does she react? She moves toward him to talk. She seeks to do the loving thing: talk this thing through and reconcile. So she says, "I can't believe you bought me a birthday card instead of an anniversary card. This is so unloving. We need to talk." In that discussion, he gets defensive, and tries to downgrade the importance of it. That doesn't set well. She expresses herself more negatively and critically. He isn't getting it. She lets him know he is an uncaring human being.

WITHOUT LOVE
SHE REACTS
THE CRAZY CYCLE
HE REACTS
WITHOUT RESPECT

Without love she reacts without respect. To her, she is trying to get through to him that she needs to feel his love. She is feeling unloved. Can't he "see" that in her reaction? What he does "hear" in her negative criticism is that she has contempt for who he is as a man. What happens to the other side of that coin?

Without respect he reacts. He needs respect like he needs air to breathe. When the fawn sits on his air hose, he will react. How does he react? He tends to move away, not wanting to talk. He seeks to do the respectful thing: protect the relationship by preventing this conflict escalating into a hurtful fight. He tries to stop himself from reacting by withdrawing. So he says nothing. He may say, "Drop it. Forget it. Quit provoking me." She can't believe it. This hurts her. This threatens her. She feels neglected, ignored, disconnected. She moves toward him to talk about this. To him he feels even more disrespected. So, he reacts even more.

Without respect he reacts without love. He gets angry, and tells her in no uncertain terms he is done talking about it. He then exits, and says nothing about the conflict for three days. This puts her in shock. How can he not talk about this? Feeling even more unloved, she reacts. She reacts without respect by telling him he is the most unloving man on the planet. He then feels her getting historical, dredging everything up from the past after he dropped it.

Round and round it goes. Where it stops, nobody knows. Without love, she reacts without respect. Without respect, he reacts without love. Then, without love, she reacts without respect. Then, without respect, he reacts without love. You get the picture. Do you see this in your marriage?

A wife wrote, "The Crazy Cycle is a practical way of helping us identify when we have miscommunicated. Instead of identifying an unusual blow-up as (my husband) being touchy or over-reacting, this concept helped me identify ways that I may be communicating disrespect without realizing it."

"She . . . said, 'On me alone . . . be the blame.'"
– 1 Samuel 25:24

Today, some wives reject the idea that they are responsible for their disrespect. Their disrespect is caused by their husbands' lack of love. Victimization and blame placing is the name of the game: "Humpty Dumpty sat on a wall. Humpty Dumpty had a great fall. Humpty Dumpty was pushed." Is this your mindset? We are not trying to be without empathy. Shakespeare wrote, "Everyone can master a grief but he that has it." We know some women are suffering at the hands of evil men. Our frame of reference is the good-willed husband. If your husband has good will, you have power to affect him through your unconditional respect. If though, you hold onto your disrespect as his fault, and refuse to confess and make adjustments, you deprive yourself of this influence.

As a wife, will you own up to your side? We have not met a wife yet who denies that she can be nasty in the home toward her husband. PMS alone can push her over the line. She can give in to her temper (Proverbs 21:19). Few wives deny this. Sadly, though, she may do nothing about it. She is more offended by what her husband is doing than by what she is doing before the Lord. Each needs to hear a quote from an unknown source: "Temper gets you into trouble. Pride keeps you there."

If couples don't accept some of the craziness as normal, or own up to their negative and sinful reactions, troubles lurk. Each begins to store up evidence that the other has a serious problem. One couple we met is committed to remaining married. But he is harsh and she is disrespectful. Round and round they go. He refuses to deal with his lack of

> "She . . . says 'I have done no wrong.'"
> – Proverbs 30:20

> "he is such a worthless man that no one can speak to him."
> – 1 Samuel 25:17

love. Instead, he says, "I don't like the name the Crazy Cycle. It makes me feel crazy." He avoids his sin by attacking the name we gave to their cycle! Classic avoidance! The wife was less than en-
thused about the Crazy Cycle too. Why? She didn't respect her husband. He deserved her dis-
respect. In typical fashion, when people don't want to deal with root issues, they fixate on something else to avoid facing themselves. No confessions.

> "Have I covered my transgressions like Adam, By hiding my iniquity . . ." – Job 31:33

Sometimes people can't stand a description precisely because it describes them! Like roaches when the light is flipped on, they scurry to a dark corner.

For years, then, they build their case. She sees all of his unloving ways, not her disrespectful manner. He sees all of her disrespectful ways, not his unloving manner. They remain locked into the feeling of being victimized and feel indignation. Each will make the case that the problem is with the other person.

Unfortunately, a wife can gather proof at four levels around the Crazy Cycle. Level one, or at 12 o'clock, she can claim he started the marital problems by his unloving ways. Level two, or at 3 o'clock on the Crazy Cycle, she can react by demanding the two of them talk, but claim he is being unloving as he stonewalls her. Level three, 6 o'clock, when he informs her that he can't stand her disrespect, she can exclaim, "What does respect have to do with it? The problem is with you. You are so unloving!" And, level four, at 9 o'clock, when he reacts by walking away from her, she can be profoundly offended and view him as the most unloving human being she knows, and that he is impossible to live with. Today, not a few women feel divorce is justified.

> "But you why do you judge your brother? Or you again, why do you regard your brother with contempt? I stand before the judgment seat of God." – Romans 14:10

At each level, she expects him to decode what is happening and be motivated to change. She feels he should confess he was wrong for being an unloving person, saying he is sorry and seeking forgiveness. He should talk to her as long as she needs to talk, not saying anything that feels unloving to her, and make a commitment to correct those areas she criticizes. His defensiveness is unjustified. She feels he is out of line. He should never tell her she is disrespectful, even if she feels no respect for him and speaks disrespectfully. She is justified for feeling this way. He brought it on. And he should never, ever walk away from her during these times because this devastates her emotionally and proves how unloving he is.

> "Therefore you have no excuse, every one of you who passes judgment, for in that which you judge another, you condemn yourself; for you who judge practice the same things."
> – Romans 2:1

But what might the Lord Jesus reveal to a wife through Paul and Peter? At each level, there could very well be another way of looking at this. Pink has her view, but blue has his view as well. Is a wife willing to discover the secret that cracks the communication code her husband is sending her?

At level four (nine o'clock), is he reacting in unloving ways because he feels she was disrespectful? Who really started it? Has she conveniently blocked out of her view what she disrespectfully said or did that triggered his unloving reaction? Is it because he wants to be loving and pleasing, but something happened in his blue view that hurt and offended him? At level one, when he reacts by going silent, is he doing so because to him this is the honorable thing to do? When feeling provoked by her criticisms and demands to talk, instead of fighting, he shuts down to stop a volatile escalation. At level two, though his silence feels very unloving to her, what does he feel when told he is extremely unloving, when he is trying to do the loving and respectful thing by not fighting? What does a husband feel when he knows his heart is in the right place only to hear that his heart is in the wrong place? At level three, when going even more quiet, what does he feel when she verbally assaults him in a way that is very disrespectful? Though she is trying to hurt him as she hurts, if he doesn't feel he was trying to hurt her, he sees her as intentionally trying to hurt him. How does this make him feel? If she uses venomous words when he would never call her such names, how offended might a husband become yet have no one defend him? How alone might he feel? How sad is he? And since men do not cry but withdraw in silence and anger, what wife decodes what is going on in his soul? If he is feeling disrespected for who he is, what is he to do? If he says, "You need to respect me" she is apt to say, "You don't deserve my respect. Right now, I have nothing but disrespect for you." If he needs her unconditional respect like she needs his unconditional love, what is he feeling deep within? If a husband devastates a wife by saying, "I respect you but don't love you," might a wife devastate a husband by saying, "I love you but don't respect you?"

> " . . . the woman is the glory of man."
> – 1 Corinthians 11:7

This is why the counsel about showing unconditional respect is so powerful. Your husband needs to be assured that you do not despise him for who he is as a man but wish to contribute to his need to feel significant in your eyes. He is in glory when you admire him. You alone have that leverage. Though he does not feel this way all the time, at those moments of intense conflict, he secretly wonders what you really feel about him. "Does she really honor me for who I am as a man?" Again, he rarely surfaces this for fear you'll say, "Of course I don't respect you." That phrase is so distressing to a man, he won't put himself in a situation to seek reassurance from you. As a wife, you feel free to seek reassurance that he loves you. He is supposed to love you, doing so unconditionally. You have every right to ask, "Do you love me?" But if he asked, "Do you respect me?" you are apt to be less than enthusiastic. You are likely to avoid answering. Besides, for him to ask appears self-glorifying. Again, he knows you love him. That's not called into question. What he secretly doubts is if you like, respect, and admire him. Just as a husband can be a loving person yet let his wife wonder if he really loves her, so a wife can be a respectful person yet let him wonder if she really respects him. And if you have a son, when he grows into manhood he'll feel exactly the same way.

Respecting him may not be fair to you, but that is his need (Ephesians 5:33). Just as your disrespect de-motivates him – decreasing his fond feelings of love for you – your respect energizes him – increasing his fond feelings of love. Of course, just as you have down times, like a bad hair day, he'll have down days and will be moody. His temperament and trials can result in sadness and lack of responsiveness to you. But month-by-month, your acts of respect kindle love. Even if they do not, Christ is pleased. This is done "as to the Lord" (Ephesians 5:22,33).

Every wife has been taught that as she loves her husband he should love her more. She believes her agape-love should motivate his agape-love. In part, it does. But, neither Paul nor Peter teaches this. It is your unconditional respect that touches his heart, and convicts his heart. As the Energizing Cycle declares: Her Respect Motivates His Love.

What we are up against is a simple female view of intimacy. A wife wants to be loved by her husband. She knows if he loves her, she'll out-love him. She knows how she responds to his love. Because she feels he does not love her as she expects, she seeks ways to motivate him to be more loving. Essentially, she keeps trying to do the same loving things. Over time, she gets frustrated that her love isn't motivating him like it would motivate her. Trying a new approach, she reacts in disrespectful ways to motivate him to change and love her more.

What is going on in this story? Trisha has PMS (Pre-Menstrual Syndrome or Pre-Murder Syndrome) in a big way. She screams at Jim. She refuses to get in tune with her cycle and prepare for it. The issue to her is Jim. She is hyper critical of him. Her feelings don't lie. He never picks up his socks, he doesn't talk, he is too disengaged from their daughter, he interrupts too much, he doesn't vacuum, and he is too preoccupied with work. He needs to change. She doesn't need to be more tolerant nor focus on his good attributes. She is the loving one. If he were more loving, most of their problems would disappear. Once a month they have this big blow up, to get him to change. She feels ashamed afterwards for her despising words, but still feels that if he were more loving they'd have a good marriage.

> "Give instruction to a wise man and he will be still wiser; Teach a righteous man and he will increase his learning." – Proverbs 9:9

The risk with this is that over time, a husband will pull back. Short-term, it can wake him up, but long-term, he closes off his spirit. That would be like him saying, "I am going to withhold love to motivate her to show more respect." Some wives, though, don't see themselves paralleling this. What frustrates these wives is that they keep making love-deposits, but don't see that their disrespectful reactions make larger withdrawals. The marriage is experiencing emotional bankruptcy and the wives don't know why. Those wives need to refocus their attention. Their efforts need to be along the line of positive respect deposits. This is what energizes their husbands. It may not be fair, but it's biblical. It may not be just, but it works.

Carl Rogers called it "unconditional positive regard." He was thinking of relationships in general, but imagine what a husband feels in his soul when he doubts if his wife feels this positive regard.

Unconditional respect works because it is from God Himself. God could have commanded wives to agape-love their husbands. He does not. That silence is significant. So, this is a faith and obedience venture. If a wife loves and reveres the Lord, she will seek to love her husband the way God says: unconditionally respectful in tone, facial expression, and deeds. Truthfully, this is an issue of obedience to the woman following Christ. This is God's command. One wife who loves the Lord and who was reacting disrespectfully said, "I need somebody to tell me this. I need this challenge. What you are saying is true. In the home, I can be very disrespectful, which is breaking my heart. Not only is it pushing my husband away, my children are being hurt by this. I need this. I really do. I love the Lord but have been blind to this. As hard as this is, it is an answer to my prayers. I knew something was missing."

Reflection: Based on Ephesians 5:33a, what do you need from your husband? Based on Ephesians 5:33b, what does your husband need from you? When you feel unloved how do you tend to react? When you react that way, how does your husband react? Based on Ephesians 5:33b and 1 Peter 3:2, what is God calling you to do as a wife to stop the crazy cycle?

Assignment: To break the Crazy Cycle, we want you to say when feeling unloved, "That felt unloving to me. Did I come across disrespectfully?" You are strong enough to do this. Yes, we know  the first part is easy to say, "That felt unloving to me." This is your mother tongue. The second part can get caught in your throat. "Did I come across disrespectfully?" But if your husband is reacting in unloving ways because he feels disrespected, do you want to know this? If you could stop the craziness with that question, would you do it? Further, is your husband more likely to hear your heart about feeling unloved if you come across as one who wants to understand his need for respect? Use the phrase and watch what happens.

Discussion: Discuss in the group what your husband did in response to the statement, "That felt unloving to me. Did I come across disrespectfully?"

Section II. For the Future, What Can a Wife Do That Motivates Her Husband God's Way?

An old country preacher used to say, "I'm goin' to tell you what I'm goin' to tell you, then tell ya', and then tell ya' what I told ya'.

Here's what we're goin' to tell ya'!

One, do what you can do: speak words of respect, ask yourself the respect question, guard against a negative tone and look, and be patient.

Two, respect your husband's desires: his <u>DESIRE</u> to work and achieve in his field, to protect and provide and even die for you, to be strong, to lead and make decisions, to analyze and counsel, to have a shoulder to shoulder friendship, and to have sexual intimacy.

Three, do the 14-Day Plan. Remember to prepare 14 days before this session.

Four, write a Card: Beyond Your Words of Love, Say It His Way. The Card He'll Keep!

Five, focus on God: for truth, in prayer, and by faith.

Six, enter into accountability with another woman.

Seven, make a decision to do what empowers you.

As you read, you'll realize that you are strong in numerous areas, so you won't need to focus on them. You might skim over certain sections. But, in another area, as you read, you'll say, "That's a great idea. I never thought about that!"

Okay, now we're ready to tell ya!

Session 7. Respect is Not a Dirty Word, So Use It!

Do what you can do: speak words of respect.

Words are powerful. Have you ever said a word you immediately regretted saying? It's amazing, isn't it, how powerful a single word can be? A slip of the tongue can be more devastating than a slip on an icy sidewalk. One wrong word can get us fired from our jobs or ostracized from our communities. Remember the old schoolyard refrain: "Sticks and stones may break my bones but words can never harm me"? It's a nice idea, but let's face it, it's wishful thinking. Words can be devastating. Anyone who has ever been hurt by a word knows the devastating power words have. Scripture itself affirms this. Job asked, "How long will you torment me, And crush me with words?" (Job 19:2). Wives have humbly confessed, "I can be venomous at times." Well, the Bible echoes that sentiment: "[The tongue] is a restless evil and full of deadly poison" (James 3:8).

> "The heart of the righteous ponders how to answer, . . ."
> - Proverbs 15:28

We can remember a hurtful word for years and years! Broken bones heal relatively quickly, but the damage words do can last a long, long time. Because a husband is more compartmentalized, he can stuff this pain away and function in the face of it. Sadness comes over his heart, however. Something precious has been lost. Some men cannot put a voice or vocabulary to their feelings, but this is it.

But words can be used for good as well. In his beautiful hymn, "A Mighty Fortress is Our God," Martin Luther refers to the terrible power of the Evil One – "and armed with cruel hate, on earth is not his equal" – but then he goes on to say that "one little word will fell him." Imagine that, a single word can make the Adversary of mankind crumble! Words are powerful, and they can be used for ill or for good. We are advised to choose them wisely.

But just as much as words can be used as weapons, they can be used as balms and tonics, to lift and to bless. They can have extraordinary power that way, and among the most powerful words along these lines is the word "respect." Just using this simple word toward a husband can accomplish things you might never have dreamed possible. But we aren't used to using the word. We are only comfortable with the word "love." This needs to change.

A very good friend of ours, who has an M.A. in Counseling, wrote us her "Aha!" experience on this subject: "[My husband] was under great stress at work. A major account went with another firm. A significant employee went to another business. Certain employees were making false accusations. Through this time I felt such love for him. I was kissing him and hugging him. I told him how much I loved him. It suddenly dawned on me that I didn't mean "LOVE" but "RESPECT." I was using the wrong word. I realized what Emerson had been saying! I needed to tell him that I respected him for how he was handling this. This is what he needed to hear, but I was telling him I loved him!"

She felt respect but said love. Why? Essentially, this word has been removed from wives' vocabulary toward husbands. Again, look at the card industry. Not one card from a wife to a husband that says, "Baby, I really respect you." That is not the kind of language one hears in our love-obsessed culture. And it certainly isn't the average woman's normal language, so she doesn't speak it. Yet, this is what motivates a husband to serve and die!

Imagine what happens when a wife speaks words of honor and her husband hasn't heard this for years! We love one wife's description: "I have been starving for this kind of direction in our marriage for eleven years...let me share with you what has happened... I gave a couple of truthful explanations of 'why I respect you.' I was very sincere...the very next morning, he left a beautiful card for me... In it he detailed a worship of God for His goodness to our family. He has never left a card like that before for me... I continued slowly to add to my list of respect over the course of four or five days, dosing him up each evening. The difference was amazing. Our intimacy multiplied by 400% in one week. He was like a different animal. He started protecting me. He also generously let me buy some kitchen appliances that he had been reluctant to do before."

Respect words motivate. They are so powerful they appear to manipulate! A husband will not respond at this level all the time. He is not as expressive-responsive. The quality of the marriage will vastly improve, though. When a wife continues using the respect word, it has a very deep reassuring feeling in the soul of a good-willed husband.

As we have said earlier, just as much as the right word can bless, the wrong word can be devastatingly harmful. Consequently, as much as using the word "respect" can bless a man and motivate him to love, using the phrase "I don't respect you" can de-motivate a man to love.

Elaine confided in her girlfriend, "Tom and I are really fighting." Elaine acknowledged that she said some very cruel things to Tom to humiliate him. "I told him, 'I do not respect you. I will never respect you!' It was like some-

"Who delight in my hurt." - Psalms 40:14

one let the air out of him. I've never seen my husband cry, but he almost did at that moment. His eyes really moistened. I was so glad. Finally, I was getting through to him. He finally felt what I feel. Most of the time he responds like a cold, listless fish." However, the relationship didn't improve. He was withdrawing more and more. She couldn't believe how unloving he was becoming.

Disrespectful words can destroy a man. A *Psychology Today* article titled, "If You Don't Have Anything Nice to Say," says that good communication and verbal skills don't always benefit a marriage. Women in happy marriages use these skills to enhance the marriage, yes – but well-spoken wives in a rocky marriage tend to use their language talents to inflict pain.

Another husband had been having terrible personal struggles in his life and was giving up on himself. This caused terrific pain in his marriage. In a counseling session with this man and his wife, the wife spoke the following words in front of her husband with bitterness and disgust: "I can never respect him and do not respect him." This was as wounding to him as all of his other troubles combined. It was comparable to a husband saying with bitterness and disgust about his wife, "I can never love her and do not love her." Imagine what it would feel like to hear those words spoken about you in front of others. Would you ever recover? What wife would not die? Words are powerful!

At the beginning of the 20th century, Sigmund Freud, the inventor of psychotherapy, gave the world the bad idea that venting our feelings is always a good thing. Sometimes it's the worst thing in the world. Sometimes keeping quiet is the only good thing we can do. Today, wives are almost expected to vent their worst feelings of disrespect toward their husbands – but what husband would be able to get away with publicly saying, "I don't love my wife and never will"? We have a terrible double standard on this love and respect issue, and it has to change. Why? Because of God's revelation in Ephesians 5:33b and 1 Peter 3:2, because of a husband's need, and because some wives need to grow into women of dignity. Some women show love in their deeds, but stomp around in an undignified manner, saying things to the husband that kill his spirit toward her.

Think about another scenario with us. Which of these two is worse? The setting is a grocery store. In aisle 11, we have a five-year-old girl throwing a temper tantrum. Having had enough, the father picks her up and swats her really hard, leaving a bruise on her bottom. In aisle 12, we have a five-year-old boy throwing a temper tantrum. Having had enough, the mother screams, "I can't stand you. I wish you had never been born! I wish I could leave you here by yourself! My life is ruined because of you."

Which one is worse? That's right. That little boy's spirit was crushed. Can't you just see him running at his mommy crying, hitting her because of his inner pain? Can you imagine the pain inside him as he hears those words spoken? Can you imagine how deeply they would wound him, how deeply they would scar him? But who do you think would be arrested? The father in aisle 11 would be turned in to Social Services! Now think of your husband. There is a little boy in your husband. He is not designed by God to hear you speak venomous remarks.

One wife wept as she relayed what she did the day before their wedding. Her husband had kept information from her so she'd not get upset. But this lack of honesty had felt like a betrayal to her. And so she had lashed out at him verbally, saying every vile thing she could: "In order to get this marriage off on the right track," she said, "he needed to know in no uncertain terms that this behavior was unacceptable. I wasn't going to be treated that way." Of course she had a point. There's just one problem. The harsh words wounded him so deeply he was unable to have sex with his wife for nearly seven years. She wounded his spirit so deeply that he closed off from her. He was too vulnerable. The harsh words rang out in his spirit over the months and years and he couldn't shake them. To him, she felt like a Marine Drill Instructor. What man wants to have sex with that?

No other man would ever dare talk to him this way. Men have an honor code. Men instinctively understand what is taboo. Yet, some wives will talk to their husbands the way that mother did in the grocery store, and the culture couldn't care less. Our society tells men to get over it. "Be a man. Take it. She should be able to say anything to you if she feels you deserve it. Sticks and stones can break your bones, but words can never hurt you." That's a lie. But men won't cry. Men react differently. Either they shut down completely, or in some cases what may happen is that a husband finally pushes his wife up against the wall, as he would with his best guy friend who talked to him this way. Then she calls 911 and he's taken away in handcuffs. The guy is dead in the water. He cannot justify physically pushing her or his need to be verbally honored. Instead, he is labeled violent and arrogant. But no one seems to be troubled by the verbal poison of some wives, and what this does to the male spirit and to marriages everywhere.

Have you spoken words of disrespect? A husband is very forgiving. But you must let him hear his mother tongue for him to know you are genuine. Something good can happen in the marriage when a wife asks, "Will you forgive me for being disrespectful?" In a recent counseling session, it finally hit a young wife that in feeling unloved, she had justified her disrespectful and contemptuous outbursts. She turned and said, "Have you felt that I did not want to honor who you are as a man? I am so sorry. Please forgive me for being disrespectful." He said, "That's right. I don't feel you want to honor me." Being blown away, since she had no idea, she again asked, "Will you forgive me for being disrespectful?" With tears in his eyes, he said, "Yes. I will." Now, if a husband is bitter or has transferred his affection, these words may not get through. But if there is good will, it can transform the marriage.

Many wives are clueless about the honor code among men. When a wife does the honorable thing by seeking forgiveness for being dishonoring, it ignites the sense of honor within the man. Honor demands that he forgive, and honor demands that he become more loving and affectionate in return. We do not believe you are so vulnerable to the feeling of being unloved that you cannot do this. We believe many of you are up to the challenge. And we know you can fight for your marriage God's way. 1 Peter 3:2!

When asking for forgiveness don't say, "Will you forgive me for being unloving?" Remember, it's not that your husband thinks you are an unloving person. On the other hand, many husbands do feel disrespected. So, use the respect word, not the love word. For most women, it is easy to say, "I was unloving." That's your language. The harder thing to do is own up to your disrespect, even in the face of what you feel is his failure to love! You probably don't see yourself as unloving as he is, nor does he. So your confession, "I was an unloving person," though real, is not that impacting. It especially falls on deaf ears if you are "confessing" a lack of love in order to get him to say he is sorry for being unloving. That's manipulation, and most husbands eventually pick up on that. But when you confess, "I was disrespectful; will you forgive me?" most husbands perk up. You are speaking his language. It solicits a response. Be prepared, though, for him to want to talk about this or even agree and tell you to stop it. You've hit a raw nerve, so be woman enough to engage his feelings on this. Many women complain that men won't talk about feelings. Yes, they will. It is that those feelings are not the feelings women want men to feel! It is a sorry state when women want their husbands to talk about the feelings of love and how to increase love and how to stop unloving attitudes, but won't jump into a conversation about the feelings of respect and how to increase respect and how to stop disrespectful attitudes.

Try these two ways of seeking forgiveness. If you feel offended, say: "When you talk to me this way, it feels unloving. Are you reacting because you feel disrespected? I'm sorry for not seeing this. Will you forgive me?" If you may be the offender, say: "When I talk to you this way, I am not trying to be disrespectful. I am coming across that way though, so I'm sorry. Will you forgive me?" If you can't say these things, write a note afterwards. It can make the same impact. Because this feels so awkward, some women absolutely refuse to say it this way. Habits are so entrenched and love so permeates a wife's heart, she chokes at the last minute. She apologizes for failing to love, instead. Saying, "I'm sorry" is natural for women. You do so to reestablish and increase the feelings of love. So what about reigniting the feelings of respect? It won't hurt you. Watch what happens in the heart of your husband. This is God's means of reigniting the feelings of love in his heart! It comes via words of respect! Go ahead. Write a note. Initially, it's a bit fearful like riding a bike at first or learning to shift gears in a manual transmission. But today you don't even think about pedaling or pushing in the clutch. It is second nature. Respect talk can become as easy as eating apple pie – without the calories.

What About Him?

Let me add another angle. Are you willing to let your husband use the "respect" word? For some wives, letting their husbands use the word "respect" can be a scary proposition. But we've gotten over it and many other couples have, and we are thankful that we did.

When we find ourselves taking a whirl on the Crazy Cycle, we immediately use the respect word and the love word. Sarah needs to hear "love" and Emerson needs to hear "respect." When Emerson sees Sarah deflating, if he says, "Am I coming across unloving?" she feels understood and re-opens her spirit. When she sees Emerson deflating, if she says, "Am I coming across disrespectfully?" he feels understood and re-opens his spirit. That's just the way it works.

Here's another question. Would you let your husband use the "disrespect" word? A wife can experience incredible changes in her marriage if she encourages her husband to say to her, "That felt disrespectful to me." Without question, this will at first be difficult and can feel threatening. But the results can be extraordinary. And, let's face it. If these are his feelings, and you have preached the importance of sharing feelings, then God's call to you is to let him voice those feelings. The problem today is that some women want their husbands to express only those feelings the wives feel good about and which increase the feelings of love. As Sarah has said, "Today, some wives think marriage is all about them and their feelings. What women feel is the final word on the matter, and if the men feel something different, they're absolutely wrong and arrogant. A female regent of one of the major universities in the world told us, 'When I heard about the Love and Respect Conference and came with my husband, I thought it meant showing love and respect to wives. But I now see what is meant.'"

> "Better is open rebuke than love that is concealed."
> - Proverbs 27:5

So be bold about this and ask your husband if he would be willing to say, "That feels disrespectful to me" whenever he feels he is not being treated respectfully. The common fear, of course, is that he will attack, saying, "Yes, I do feel disrespected because you are such a disrespectful person!" All of us fear being accused of anything negative, so we tend to avoid asking questions to which the answer is likely to be negative. But if we have the faith to permit another to communicate such deeply held feelings it can work wonders. Why not ask your husband to do this?

If you permit your husband to express this, he might say, "I would like for you to point out to me when I am coming across to you unlovingly. Would you be willing to say, 'That feels unloving to me?'" Most men have a powerful sense of justice, but don't engage their wives on this level because they themselves have a fear that only their shortcomings will be addressed. They think it will always be about the husbands being unloving, not about the wives being disrespected. Over time, however, when a husband is given the freedom to express his feelings of being disrespected, he begins to feel equity entering the marriage, and amazingly he begins to listen to his wife's appeal to be more loving! Isn't that what this whole message is about? When a wife introduces this aspect, it is uncomfortable at first. It feels like she is giving him new ammunition with which to hurt her. But not so with a good-willed husband. It appeals to his sense of honor and justice.

When you make yourself accountable to your husband, do so as an equal. By that we mean, even though you feel he is unloving, don't minimize the power of your disrespect. If you approach this from the view that your husband is 90% of the problem, and your contempt for him is really only a marginal issue, you need to realize again what the Bible is saying to you about God's call on your life. Read again Ephesians 5:33b and 1 Peter 3:2. Just because you feel that you are showing a ton of love and an ounce of disrespect doesn't mean that that's what God feels about the matter. It's human nature for each of us to minimize our sins and maximize the sins of those who are hurting us. Don't fall into that trap. Your call from God is to focus on "respect" and "respectful behavior." God would not be so clear and specific about this if it was merely some fringe matter. Your disrespect can be much more of the problem than you ever dreamed. Trust what Scripture has to say on this subject and see what happens.

One couple we know introduced these two phrases into their marriage: "That felt unloving" and "That felt disrespectful." The wife wrote, "Before we went to the retreat we realized that we had both been using communication methods that had not served us...and were harming our relationship. [My husband] can be very harsh and direct and that is difficult for me. He is also very quick to make negative comments. These things put me on the defensive... He felt that I was not being respectful when I was like that and so you see – The Crazy Cycle in all its glory! We have decided to use little triggers like 'what you are doing/saying is making me feel unloved' or 'when you do such and such, I feel you are being unloving to me.' He has told me that he would like to feel more respected and I am trying to be more aware of his need... He commented to me that he was not speaking my 'love language' and that he would like to do better in that area, and frankly, I would like that too. So I think at the beginning we will have to verbally tell each other what it is we need. Eventually we will get better at knowing what the other needs and to see the visual signals. We have asked each other for forgiveness in our shortcomings and that was a great feeling. We are using 'trigger phrases' to let the other know they are crossing the line and that by doing so, the person can back off before the cycle begins. We are also being more respectful to each other and not so quick to speak without thinking."

This is the commencement of mutual accountability.

So if you speak words of respect – and encourage your husband to speak about respect – a relationship can change overnight. We are not exaggerating. All a wife needs to do is try it. If, though, you hang onto the feeling that the respect word is antiquated and refuse to use it, you deprive yourself of God's means of motivating your husband to feel fond feelings of love for you.

Reflection: What do you feel about using the respect word? What do you feel about asking, "Will you forgive me for coming across disrespectfully?"

Assignment: Say something respectful to your husband. Or, after coming across disrespectfully (which we are not encouraging!) ask, "Will you forgive me for coming across disrespectfully?"

Discussion: Share with one another a "respect word" you used on your husband. What did you notice happening in him?

Was that hard for you to do? Why or why not? What did you feel if you asked him to forgive you for coming across disrespectfully? How did he respond?

Extra Discussion: How are you coming with that statement, "That felt unloving to me. Did I come across disrespectfully?" Is he engaging you on that question, albeit negatively by blaming you for his lack of love? Are you remaining calm? Stay with it. If he says, "Yes, I reacted because you're disrespectful," don't panic. If this is true, you need to know it. If it is untrue, watch what happens. One day you will hear, "No, you didn't do anything, it was my fault. I'm sorry."

Session 8. Before you Act, Ask Yourself A Question!

Do what you can do: ask yourself the respect question.

Oh, if only a wife would meditate prior to speaking or acting!

Human beings are creatures of habit. At first we are very conscious of things – as we said earlier about bike riding or manual shifting – but soon enough we become so accustomed to what we are doing that we are utterly unconscious. It has become a habit and an instinct. The culture we live in is so instinctively love-oriented that it will take some time for wives to unlearn their habitual instincts to always go in that direction. So at first we must be very deliberate. One way in which we must be deliberate is in asking what we call the "respect question."

> "Every prudent man acts with knowledge, . . ."
> - Proverbs 13:16
> " . . . the prudent man considers his steps."
> - Proverbs 14:15

Ask yourself a simple question before speaking or acting: "Is that which I am about to do or say going to result in my husband feeling respected or disrespected?" In most cases, this question has been removed from the marital radar screen. If you really think about it though, asking this question should be second nature – and with a little effort, in time it will be. But for most wives it sounds and feels entirely foreign.

Some wives feel that asking this question tacitly declares their husbands to be somehow superior to them, so they wouldn't dream of asking it. But the reality is that a wife is not letting go of power in asking this question anymore than a husband is letting go of power when he asks "Is that which I am about to do or say going to result in her feeling loved or unloved?" On the contrary, it is extraordinarily empowering. Every wife yearns for her husband to ask the "love question." When her husband comes across lovingly, a wife is deeply touched. So, too, a husband is deeply – almost involuntarily – motivated by a wife's respect. Asking this question keeps you conscious of what you are about to do. You'll be genuinely amazed at how powerful that simple question is in creating a whole new atmosphere in your marriage. Men subconsciously ask this question in their dealings with other men. For them it is a well-worn groove and it feels much more natural to stay in it and be respectful than to go out of it and be disrespectful. They instinctively know that if they come across disrespectfully, they will terribly damage their relationships.

For wives, as we have established, this respectful impulse is less instinctual. A wife wrote, "I totally understand what you are saying about speaking a foreign language to women about respect. As I sat at the conference and listened to you speak, I had no problem hearing and agreeing with everything you were saying about men (needing to love). No questions asked, that was my husband's (inadequacy) to the letter. Then on Saturday, when you started talking about respect and the lack there of, I have to be honest, I was taken aback. I have been so focused on why he couldn't understand me, that I was totally missing that he was feeling put down. I think this is especially true for me, as a mother of young children. I am forever trying to make them understand right from wrong and why things are the way they are. I never realized that I could and had been projecting that onto my husband as well. In all honesty, I don't think (my husband) really knew exactly how to explain how my behavior was really making him feel."

This wife had been totally focused on being loved and showing love, not on showing respect. She was not mean or ugly, just unaware. So when she introduced this Respect Question into her mind, positive things began to happen.

Another wife wrote, "The whole respect thing was such a foreign language to me that I really didn't understand the ways that I was causing trouble in my own marriage and thinking that (my husband) was the problem because he was 'touchy' in certain areas. Because the respect thing isn't the main issue for women, looking at things from that angle is truly like moving into a different language and culture. It takes work. It isn't particularly fun. It feels like you are going against the grain of what is 'normal' and if you are feeling unloved at the moment (which is how you feel if your man just blew up in your face over 'nothing'), well, you don't feel very motivated to make the extra effort to speak and act in a different, more respectful way."

The biggest struggle a wife has when feeling unloved is to react respectfully. That seems to be a contradiction of terms to some women. To feel unloved by a husband is to feel no respect for that husband! To react respectfully when feeling unloved seems something like enjoying a dentist drilling a hole in your tooth without Novocain. When in pain, who wants to ask, "Is that which I am about to say or do going to feel respectful to him?" Who in their right mind would introduce that question into their worldview? The answer is simple: the woman who loves God and His Word, who knows God loves her and would never steer her wrong, would never tell her to do something that will not end up blessing her. Again, we return to Ephesians 5:33 and 1 Peter 3:1,2.

Ephesians 5:33 **Nevertheless let each individual among you also love his own wife even as himself; and let the wife see to it that she respect her husband.**
1 Peter 3:1,2 **...you wives... even if any of them are disobedient to the word, they may be won without a word by the behavior of their wives, as they observe your... respectful behavior.**

Reflection: Until now, did you ever consider asking the Respect Question before speaking or acting? If not, since Scripture makes this central in marriage, have you considered what contributed to this lack of premeditation? Why are some Christian women unthinking when it comes to obeying Ephesians 5:33 and 1 Peter 3:1,2?

Assignment: This week make a decision to ask yourself, "Is that which I am about to do or say going to result in my husband feeling respected or disrespected?" Ask the question!

Discussion: Share an incident in which you asked yourself "The Respect Question" prior to acting or reacting. What happened?

Session 9. Not What You Say, But How You Say It!
(The Respect Look & Tone)

Do what you can do: guard against a negative tone/look.

If looks could kill... How many times have you heard that phrase? Sour looks, scornful looks, looks of disrespect kill the tender spirits inside men – and looks kill marriages.

> "She has despised you and mocked you, . . .
> She has shaken her head behind you, . . ."
> - Isaiah 37:22

Dr. Gottman, whom we have previously referenced, wrote, "Wives who make sour facial expressions when their husbands talk are likely to be separated within four years." Think about that. You can be full of love, but your look can express profound hostility, contempt and disrespect. Many men see in that unconscious sour look contempt for who they are as men. We are not saying that these feelings are correct, only that this is how many men react to a wife's facial language. In the book **Why Marriages Succeed or Fail**, Gottman says that contempt is "perhaps the most corrosive force in marriage" (p. 61). And this is not a mere observation on his part. Extensive research backs him up in making the point.

> "The refined and delicate woman among you, who would not venture to set the sole of her foot on the ground for delicateness and refinement, shall be hostile toward the husband she cherishes . . ."
> - Deuteronomy 28:56

Wives, guard against that sour look. You know the one we're talking about – and if you don't, get to know it. It's your own worst enemy.

And just as harmful as a look can be, a tone of voice can be devastating. Be aware of how you look and sound to your husband. Even if your actual words are not so hurtful, your tone of voice and facial expressions can say it all. What's really at issue here is your attitude. If your attitude toward your husband is disrespectful, it will be hard for you to hide it. And many wives don't see why on earth they should hide it. They believe their husbands will see it as a cry for love and will be able to decode it as such. But as we have said, most husbands don't decode this. They are more apt to react by shrinking from you, deflating, and shutting down. A woman who understands this is well along the way toward changing the destructive habits in her marriage.

One wife wrote after the Love and Respect Conference, "I learned so much and it's been helpful. I came to the conference alone, because my husband did not want to go. I was very angry with him and God for a day or so, but then came to the conference anyway. It helped me put things back in perspective. I haven't blatantly done the respect thing, but have tried to change my attitude toward my husband, and it is working. We...have become extremely close lately. I just wanted to say thank you for what you and Sarah do. Keep up the good work!"

> "Adorn yourself with eminence and dignity, And clothe yourself with honor and majesty." – Job 40:10

Another wife wrote, "Most wives do not say, 'Help me with better communication skills so I can communicate more respectfully to my husband.' But that is what I want to do."

Are you willing to make some minor changes? Are you sorry for some of the negative attitudes in the past? Do you see that even if you didn't mean to hurt your husband with your scornful look, that's what happened anyway?

The question was asked of a Sunday school class, "What is repentance?" One girl said, "It is being sorry for your sins." Another little boy said, "It is being sorry enough to quit." There is a difference between remorse and repentance. May we encourage you to turn the corner on a negative attitude?

> "...change my tone..."
> - Galatians 4:20

Think right now about what you will do yet today. Don't delay! If you have a look of disgust, disdain, and disrespect, few men warm up to that. But a simple change of your look or attitude can go a long way.

Even though you will fail at this sometimes, don't quit! God is on your side. Remember Proverbs 24:16 "For a righteous man falls seven times, and rises again." If you fall, get up again. It's worth it. Your toddler when learning to walk would fall but get back up. Fall and get back up. Your toddler didn't lay down one day and refuse to get back up. That was never an option. In *Mere Christianity*, C.S. Lewis said, "After each failure, ask forgiveness, pick yourself up, and try again. Very often what God first helps us towards is not the virtue itself but just this power of always trying again." For some of you, this is a deeper issue than your marriage. God is using your marriage to deepen your relationship with Christ. The Bible says, "And let endurance have its perfect result, that you may be perfect and complete, lacking in nothing" (James 1:4).

The tone of a woman's voice has great power in her relationship. Disrespectful vocal inflections grind at a man on a profound level. Men don't feel good about that tone any more than women feel good about a man's harshness. The only reason a man responds to the complaint is to hush that tone. Of course, you can inaccurately deduce, "Aha! My tone of voice works!" It works like Samson's wife's harassment worked: "And it came about when she pressed him daily with her words and urged him, that his soul was annoyed to death" (Judges 16:16)." But this is a very bad conclusion, which can begin a very bad habit. Annoying and disrespectful tones work at one level, but they sacrifice something at another level. The critical tone will work in the short-term, but in the long-term it will hurt you and hurt your marriage. Over time, you'll wonder why he does not make you feel special like he used to do. You must remember, that when courting, you never spoke with that tone. Take the time to invest in your marriage over the long haul. Sacrifice immediate satisfaction for long-term satisfaction. It takes a bit of faith, but everything good does.

Here's an immediate change you can introduce. Say respectfully, "That felt unloving to me." Sarah will do this. If she says in a disrespectful tone, "You are such an unloving human being!" that isn't received by Emerson. Sarah has said before, "I can be right in what I am saying but wrong for the way I say it." Wives are more verbal and will inevitably tend toward complaints and criticism. Be careful! You may have fallen victim to the cultural mindset that says it's all right to vent negative feelings toward your husband, that it's okay to say things to him you wouldn't dream of saying to anyone else. Some wives become convinced that their husbands won't change unless they speak disrespectfully to get his attention. But believe us: a wife cannot motivate a husband to be loving in tone and words by her disrespectful tone and words. Good ends are not to be achieved via bad means. One has to give in order to receive. That's God's rule, not ours.

> "Give, and it will be given to you. . . . For by your standard of measure it will be measured to you in return." – Luke 6:38

Reflection: Think of those moments your husband frustrates and hurts you. Think of your negative reaction. Do you believe your disrespectful tone and look should be clearly understood by your husband as a cry to him to be more sensitive and loving? Or might he think you secretly despise who he is as a human being?

Assignment: We want you to role-play in the mirror when no one is around. Recall what you were feeling when your husband hurt you the last time and you reacted disrespectfully. In the mirror, reenact your disrespectful reaction. Replay your facial expressions and tone. Listen to yourself and watch yourself. Don't be afraid to do this. Effective communicators do this. Such an exercise can be very enlightening.

Discussion: Share your observations of the role-play with the group. Someone volunteer to role-play the disrespectful wife and another portray the husband. As the wife who role-played, what were you expecting your husband to see? As the one who was the husband, getting into the male skin, what did you feel when she came at you this way? Discuss the extent to which you as a wife can project a disrespectful look and speak disrespectfully in tone when feeling unloved? How many of you expect your husband to see underneath to your hurting heart? How easy is that for a husband? If you have a son, how easy will that be for him if his wife comes at him with contempt? Is it true that no man would talk to another man the way a wife will sometimes talk to her husband? Why do men not talk to each other this way? How are some of you communicating the intensity of your emotions in a respectful way?

Session 10. Relax, You'll Get There!

Do what you can do: be patient.

As we have said, many of the women who have applied some of these techniques have experienced immediate, startling results. Others have not. And yet the simple fact of the matter is that eventually, inevitably, amazingly this stuff works with a good-willed man. Of course, as Christians we're not supposed to do things because they work, but because they are right, because they are what God desires for us to do. When we obey God, it's never principally about the results, it's principally about obedience and faith and trust. Of course results usually follow, but not always exactly as we might like. So be patient if this isn't happening on the timetable you had in mind. And continue

> " . . . in former times the holy women . . . who hoped in God, . . ."
> - 1 Peter 3:5
> " . . . surely now my husband will love me."
> - Genesis 29:32
> "Now this time my husband will become attached to me, . . ."
> - Genesis 29:34
> ". . . now my husband will dwell with me, . . ."
> - Genesis 30:20

to be optimistic. We encourage you to be even more optimistic than ever. God's Word does not disappoint. But God knows that we are naturally impatient creatures, so He tells us to take heart and to be patient.

Be especially encouraged because when you do what God wants you to do, you are sowing for the long term. Any women's magazine will give you short-term ways of dealing with your spouse, but these magazines don't get their ideas from Scripture, and they don't worry about what happens in the long term. They are interested in selling magazines now, this month. But God's Word is all about the long term. It's about reaping a glorious harvest because you took the time to plant things the right way and wait until the crops bore fruit. This is not about short-term control but about long-term fruitfulness. You may have some wonderful short-term results – and praise God for them – but overall you should take the long view. And keep doing what you do unto the Lord, who loves you and is with you, alongside you, in the midst of your struggles. Be of good cheer and trust Him to bring about the results in His timing.

Do you have hope in God? Do you have hope in the truth of God's Word? How can a wife be pessimistic about this revelation from God? This is His answer! Yet, as with all spiritual truth that is applied, patience is needed. God is not some genie who will transform your marriage with a clap of the hands. It's not as if you will show respect for fifteen seconds, and presto, your husband will love you romantically forever! Remember, your husband is not expressive-responsive. In other words, he is not a woman. Don't expect him to become sentimental. Don't blurt out, "See, it isn't working. I married a romantic imbecile!" You are expecting something from God's Word that God's Word does not promise. Be patient. Be positive. Let God's truth do in your husband's spirit what God intends for respect to do.

Ready yourself. One wife wrote, "I'm convinced that this is true and revolutionary, but it will take time, prayer, and diligence to build it into our marriage and to keep it there." The challenge to be optimistic and patient when you've been conditioned to see men as flawed and undeserving of respect is very hard. You'd prefer to drink castor oil. If you hold your husband responsible for the negativity, and believe that you are negative because he is "unloving" why would you be optimistic, patient, or receptive? When a new idea challenges the status quo, the greater the chance this idea will be met with resistance. Some of you have probably been formulating reasons why this respect message is invalid even while reading. That is normal to a point. It can be an uphill battle; respecting husbands runs contrary to the romantic status quo. Who wants to be long-suffering and sanguine? Even so, God has revealed this inestimable truth. Always remember, that this is God's idea for you, not Sarah and Emerson's idea for you. Faith in God is the key to patience.

What if we said your lack of optimism and patience is causing the collapse of your marriage, would this get your attention? May we remind you of what our friend wrote earlier? "Remember me? I'm the one with all the Harvard degrees who had never heard of the concept of unconditional respect. Your message has had a profound, positive impact on our marriage... I have tried to understand the meaning of unconditional respect and to really respect (my husband). I've had the opportunity to observe in other couples the destructiveness of the wife's lack of respect. I believe that you're onto something huge here...what is really revolutionary in your message is the concept of unconditional respect... The respect message itself is really gender neutral: we both owe each other unconditional respect, it's just that the men give it more easily and need it more... It seems that in the old 'woman, obey me' context the women often were treated with neither love nor respect. Now our society has swung in the opposite direction to a love-dominated marriage model and the men are suffering the most..."

Of course, many wives will flat-out reject what this woman is saying. They would say that the men are certainly not suffering the most – and the wives are not being destructive! Whatever the truth is, we know that as long as these wives continue to blame their husbands, they will not act on this message. And if they do manage to act on it for a little while, their fundamental lack of patience with it will soon cause them to revert to their previous ways. One wife said: "I'll show unconditional respect for a little while but if he doesn't change, forget it." So much for unconditional! This same woman would probably be spitting mad if her husband said, "I'll show unconditional love for a little while, but if she doesn't change, forget it." We should practice what we preach. Again, the Bible teaches BOTH unconditional love and unconditional respect.

But other wives will make a new choice. This woman with all the Harvard degrees did, and the results have been profound and positive. There has to be a paradigm shift. A decision needs to be made that we will hope in God and believe that when we act on His Word, over the marathon of the marriage, good things will result. Some women sabotage the whole process with gloom and doom, and a lack of fortitude and forbearance. One woman we know decided to do the Respect Test. Storming into the room in which he was seated, she said, "I was thinking about you, and the things I respect. I want you to know I respect you." She stood there and stared at him. He was so self-conscious as she glared at him, it unnerved him and he said nothing. She then told me, she grabbed him by the collar and said, "Come into the other room. This didn't work. We need to talk."

We were in shock. What was she thinking? Her whole demeanor discredited the message, and what on earth was she doing grabbing him like that? We could only conclude she didn't want it to work. It's like the person who says,

"Okay, I'll pray this so-called sinners prayer and accept God into my life, but if things don't change pronto – and I mean right away – I'm bagging the whole dumb thing!" Someone like that isn't giving anything a fair chance at all. They might be fooling themselves, but they are not fooling God. In the deepest recesses of her heart, this woman did not believe this could be true, and she wasn't about to let it be true, not if she could help it. If it worked, it would demand of her to become a dignified woman. Though she wanted him to be a loving human being regardless of her behavior, she did not want to become a respectful woman regardless of *his* behavior. She did not want to memorize 1 Timothy 3:11. "Women must likewise be dignified." We grieve for women who feel so horrible about the concept of unconditional respect that in order not to feel worse, they subvert the process so they can claim their husbands are at fault. They have hardened themselves against the precious Word of God and there's little anyone can do about it if they keep reacting this way.

Of course not all wives who resist this teaching are like that woman. Some wives are simply afraid, and that's a natural reaction. This is what one wife wrote to us after a conference: "At one point on Saturday afternoon (at the Love and Respect Conference), I felt a little afraid. I realized that these principles, if practiced, would change our relationship. We've had a good marriage for over twenty years, but we have each kept a piece of ourselves to ourselves. In going down this path, I think our marriage will be much closer – a part of me was afraid of the change or the risk. I know in my heart the change will be for the better – but still change can be a little frightening."

God bless her for being honest. There's nothing wrong with admitting to fear about any of this. We are all flawed human beings, and sometimes we are almost more willing to put up with an awful situation than we are making a new path. We need

> " . . . do what is right without being frightened by any fear."
> – 1 Peter 3:6

encouragement. That's one of the reasons we think it's so important for women who are serious about this to find other women who will do this with them and share the ups and downs of it with them.

So be honest. You may be fearful. But will your fear override your obedience to God's Word? Or will you allow yourself to get excited about this, to trust that doing what's right rarely goes wrong?

One wife's evaluation of our message was this: "I am a counselor, and I still had no idea that males had such a deep need... Now my husband's reactions make sense to me... 'What was unclear?' Nothing – it helped to have everything related back to Scripture... 'Do you plan to tell a friend to attend the Love and Respect conference?' I will tell them they need to go – these concepts are too important to their relationship, but we don't hear them at all in our day-to-day interaction. Thank you so much for changing the course of our marriage. This is the most worthwhile thing I have done since we've been married. God bless you!"

When information about men is shared, some women move into shame. In a *U.S. News & World Report* article we read the following: "Research shows that boys and girls are different in terms of experiencing shame. Typically females have a greater tendency to feel shame over failing at something than males do. The reason is that a girl is more likely to blame herself than a boy would be. She feels ashamed, but he analyzes the action. This gender difference can cause problems in a marital relationship later on. If a husband criticizes something his wife has done, she may interpret it as a criticism of herself and get angry or depressed about it." ("The Anatomy of Shame," by Alvin Sanoff. March 9, 1992. Page 56.)

Don't let shame come over you. Do not personalize this information to mean you have failed your husband, children, yourself, the universe, mankind and God! These truths are from God to serve you, not shame you. This is God's gift of knowledge and wisdom to you. "Every good thing bestowed...is from above, coming down from the Father..." (James 1:17). Move forward in faith and patience.

> ". . . let him who thinks he stands take heed lest he fall." – 1 Corinthians 10:12

Here is another loving warning. Optimism can surge when you apply these things, but get ready for a period where things go flat. A woman wrote, "We have met with some couples and personally shared the Love and Respect information. They grasp it marvelously, seem to do a turnaround and then they fall flat."

I, Emerson, told her to let them know that "they fall flat" because it was so easy the first time. In war, if troops are too victorious at first, it lulls them into a complacency that is deadly. When troops parachute into enemy territory and there are no casualties, their intensity lessens. The mind, body, and heart relax too much. As the troops proceed, they can be ill-prepared for the next battle. The sense of well-being deceives them. It can prove deadly. Short-term victory can be worse than a near defeat. When success is easily won, troops let down. The weakest moment can come after the strongest moment. They become passive.

When applying "respect," success comes quickly and easily. So the wife relaxes. "Oh, I did it. This worked. My spouse is loving me now." For example, as a wife chooses to put on respect, her husband melts and puts on love. The wife then feels fantastic. "He loves me!" She then expects him to keep showing love. When he doesn't, she reacts without respect instead of putting on respect! Then, without respect, he reacts without love. The Crazy Cycle! She needs to return to what she did at first: expect of herself to put on respect in the face of un-love. One wife wrote, "Once we experience a little success, we are apt to 'rest on our laurels' and neglect the continued self-discipline needed for continued success."

Easy success unwisely relaxes us. We then get crushed when a new battle arises! Oh, that we would take two steps forward, and not be in shock when we slide one step back. Proverbs 24:16 says, "For a righteous man falls seven times, and rises again." The difference between couples with great marriages and those with bad marriages isn't the absence of conflict. Successful couples rebound quickly and start again. Unsuccessful couples get discouraged and angry and withdraw into stubbornness, refusing to start over. They close off to God and one another. Satisfying and stable marriages see "failure" as part of success. Hall of Fame batters miss 7 out of 10 times! Babe Ruth struck out more than anybody. But he didn't quit. Successful couples do not let the loss of a battle drive them to the conclusion that they have lost the war. Nor do they let temporary victories lull them into a false sense of security.

One person wrote, "The reason we came (to the conference) was because my pastor found out that I had filed for divorce. And he asked if I would go see you. I was so bitter at this point I told my pastor that I would apply it in my next marriage. He said, 'Okay, I'll pay for the weekend. Just go!' And I really thought nothing you would say could change my mind. It was the most eye-opening weekend of my life. (My wife) and I both wanted the divorce, but we really had no good reason; (we were) just unhappy. Your conference turned on all kinds of light bulbs for both of us. And it saved our marriage. Emerson, God is using you in a big way. I just wanted to say thank you."

Sadly, though, after receiving this note, several weeks later this couple got in a major conflict and divorced. After the divorce, both realized how wrong and foolish they had been. People can receive the insights from the Love and Respect Conference, and experience an incredible healing, but just that quickly, re-enter their destructive paths.

Be sure to also guard against this wife's experience. She approached her husband: "I told my husband that I wasn't trying to dishonor him, but that I needed help and guidance on how to react more respectfully to him. I then broke down and cried, dumping on him all the hurts that are inside of me. So out of my need for understanding, I forced him to not only carry his hurts but mine. I really failed him again, as he went silent." Some wives start out extremely well, but a few minutes in the conversation, they lose their steadfastness and revert to the old pattern of negatively crying out for understanding. Instead of seeking to understand the husband, and acting on that understanding, there is a return to demanding that he be more understanding of her hurts. Wives can be stronger than this, but we sometimes feel we haven't challenged them, so this weepiness gets the better of them. When we challenge some wives along this line, amazingly they testify to how a weight lifted from them. They realize it is okay for them to be more forbearing and to stop the periodic wailing.

Reflection: Are you easily defeated after you've been disrespectful? Do you let defeat defeat you? According to Proverbs 24:16, a righteous person may fall seven times but she gets back up. Is God calling you to get back up like your toddler? What advantage is there in getting back up? Envision for a moment that you are mad and feeling disdain. See yourself spouting off all kinds of mean superlatives. What did that accomplish? Now envision yourself pulling back and rebounding; not stepping over the line into disrespectful comments and looks. In fact, see yourself saying something positive. What does that achieve? Remember the Scriptures. After his section on marriage, Peter writes, "not returning evil for evil, or insult for insult, but giving a blessing instead; for you were called for the very purpose that you might inherit a blessing" (1 Peter 3:9). We also learn in Proverbs 17:14 "The beginning of strife is like letting out water, So abandon the quarrel before it breaks out." See yourself doing this in obedience to God.

Assignment: This week just when you are about to be disrespectful, study yourself. Do you have an inner script that you follow? "Well, forget this respect stuff. I am not going to rebound. I am out of patience. My husband is hopeless. I could care less. I'm going to verbally dump. I've been sitting on this too long. This respect teaching stinks. He deserves a good tongue lashing." There is not one wife who is always respectful any more than there is a husband who loves perfectly. You will have such moments. But will you keep having those moments by following your inner script? Ask yourself, "Do I have to react this way? Is this the only way that will motivate him to change? Is this about him changing, or is this about me being out of control?" Is God calling you to trust Him? Is the Lord saying, "You are a dignified and loving person. Do not succumb to belligerent and contemptuous reactions. Start again, and improve each time. The future is worth it, not only for your own inner peace, but for your marriage and your children."?

Discussion: Share what you are learning about patience and rebounding. Also, are you getting in tune with the value of doing this unto Christ? If you take your eyes off the Lord, what happens? After you stumble, share what you are doing to get back up and start again before things get out of hand. Share your new inner script.

Session 11: His Conquests: respecting his desire to work and achieve in his field

Understand Your Husband's Desires

Do you understand your husband's desires? His desire to work and achieve in his field? His desire to protect and provide, and even die for you? His desire to be strong, to lead and make decisions? His desire to analyze and counsel? His desire for a shoulder-to-shoulder friendship? And his desire for sexual intimacy?

We've talked a lot about why showing a husband respect can motivate him to love, but we haven't said very much about what is going on in him that stimulates this. Nor have we said much about specific ways of doing this. One wife wrote, "Men hear lots of examples elsewhere of how they can be more loving. If you could add any additional practical examples of how women disrespect men without meaning to, or how to disagree respectfully, that would be helpful. It is such a foreign concept that we women have a hard time knowing how to apply it."

Let's look at the positive side of this question, and share from the Bible six dimensions that show respect. When a wife grasps the wisdom of Scripture about her husband, and acts on this, a husband is motivated. To make this memorable, we use the acronym C.H.A.I.R.S. This defines men's desires in relationships as: Conquests, Hierarchy, Authority, Insight, a Shoulder-to-Shoulder Relationship, and Sexuality. (You can learn more about this by ordering the Love and Respect Marriage Conference from our web site, www.loveandrespect.com.) When you show your husband you want to understand his needs, he'll be more responsive to your appeal to understand your needs. This is a basic law of relationships. Men respond to honorable appeals to be fair.

Since Peter and Paul conclude their sections on marriage with a husband's need for respect, apparently this is the deepest need within a husband, given he is assured of his wife's love. The question then becomes, how can a wife show respect? Does the Bible give us any specific insights?

Interestingly, neither Paul or Peter define respect. They assume every wife knows what it is and what it isn't. Having said that, the following can be extremely helpful in understanding how to show respect to your husband. If you respect his desires in the following areas, even though his performance isn't always great, you will ignite fond feelings of love in your husband. If he is good-willed toward you, watch what will happen.

His Conquests: Respecting His Desire to Work and Achieve in the Field.

Understand your husband's desire to work and achieve in his field.

God created Adam "to cultivate and keep" the garden (Genesis 2:15). This was even before Eve was created. In other words, God created Adam to

> " . . . the Lord God took the man and put him into the garden of Eden to cultivate it and keep it." – Genesis 2:15

work. When one man meets another man for the first time, one usually asks, "What do you do?" Almost inevitably, men define themselves in terms of their work. Even the curse in Genesis 3 came to men differently than it did to women. Women are cursed in the family (Genesis 3:16), men are cursed in the field (Genesis 3:17-19). In the first chapters of the Bible – at the very dawn of human history – a husband is principally defined by his work "in the field". Similarly Eve derives the largest part of her significance through family. Generally when women meet for the first time they ask each other, "Are you married? How many children do you have?"

> "Then the Lord God said, 'It is not good for the man to be alone; I will make him a helper suitable for him.'" – Genesis 2:18
> " . . . for indeed man was not created for the woman's sake, but woman for the man's sake." – 1 Corinthians 11:9

Of course in the last century women have entered the workplace in record numbers, especially in modern Western culture, and many women find increasing measures of their own significance through work. And yet – generally speaking – wives still find their fundamental identity in relation to their families.

Going back to the first chapters of Genesis, Eve was created by God to be a suitable helper. She was to come alongside of Adam, especially as it related to his work in the garden. Whatever her own career goals, every woman when dating sends a strong message to her future husband, "I believe in your pursuits. I admire you for them. I respect who you are in this area." There is something powerful and magical about this dynamic. The man swells with pride at the idea of this wonderful woman believing in him and casting her lot with him. She will be his cheerleader, the one who believes in him when others don't, the one who sees that he is a success, that he will be a success. And part of this magical confidence that he feels from her belief in him and what he does comes from the idea that she will always feel this way.

But all too often after marriage, as a wife's focus on the family takes over, her interest in what her husband does in the field can wane significantly. In fact, she can feel it competes with the family. Or, worse, she begins to see her husband as a failure in the field and a failure in his role in the family. At that point, without exception, the husband shuts down. He is extraordinarily vulnerable in this area.

To respect a husband means appreciating his desire to work and achieve in the field. When a wife does this, it generally creates fond feelings of love in the husband's heart over the marathon of the marriage. As a woman, the wife may instinctively underestimate the power of this dynamic in her marriage. That's because, as we have said again and again, her feelings of love are ignited quite differently.

In our *Love & Respect* marriage conferences, we say that a wife spells love C.O.U.P.L.E, the acronym we use stands for: Closeness, Openness, Understanding, Peacemaking, Loyalty, and Esteem. (Go to www.loveandrespect.com for more information.) Each letter is based on key Scriptures pertaining to wives. Peter teaches that a husband is to treat his wife in a special way precisely "since she is a woman" (1 Peter 3:7). The implication is clear. Men and women have different needs. The other side of the equation is that husbands have unique needs. What a wife needs to understand is that God created them male and female. Her husband is not wrong just different.

Take the following story. Belinda and Tom are struggling financially. She is upset over their limited income, especially insofar as there is almost no money to spend on decorating, something extremely dear to her heart. As Tom walks into the house one day after work , he sees that Belinda is distressed. "What's wrong?" he asks. She has been

"Then Jacob's anger burned against Rachel, . . ." – Genesis 30:2

THE
CRAZY
CYCLE

WITHOUT LOVE

SHE REACTS

HE REACTS

WITHOUT RESPECT

thinking about the answer to this question for some time, long before he asked it. So she glares at him and says, "If you had a better job with more income, we could do some really nice things to this home. I sometimes wonder what it would be like if I didn't have to pinch pennies all the time. My sister just built a new home, and look at what I have!" She rolls her eyes in exasperation. Tom can't believe his ears. He feels stabbed. "Why does she put me down?" he wonders. "I work as hard as I can. She doesn't feel I'm good enough for her. Everybody respects me but her." Quickly his hurt turns into anger. "Yeah, well, nobody better would marry you!" he yells. Then he leaves. Belinda eats alone, feeling completely misunderstood and even more unloved than before. That's a classic example of the Crazy Cycle in action, and it all started because, without realizing it, Belinda disrespected Tom in a key area. Predictably, he reacted unlovingly and stormed off in full retreat.

A husband's self-image is directly connected to his work efforts and conquests. A husband deflates when his wife suggests he is a loser and not a winner, or is failing and not succeeding. He feels dishonored when his work is viewed as a trivial pursuit compared to the family needs or her career. On the other hand, he feels respected when she appreciates his call from God to cultivate his garden for her and the family. This touches his heart and motivates him to move toward her in love. When he does not feel this respect, he does not feel energized by her. He'll react negatively. For instance, writing a note that says, "I admire you for working. Every day you get up and work. Thank you." That is a huge deposit, especially with a man feeling he is a meal ticket. Try this yourself, and watch what happens.

Reflection and

Discussion: Is your husband trying to say the following to you? Discuss why this is or is not his statement to you: "Dream with me. Be supportive of my goals and life aims. Get excited about my adventures – don't conclude that when I share my dreams with you that I am going out tomorrow to do it. Tell me that you see my personal competencies, or at least my potential.

Praise me for my diligence in working. Notice my successful results. I am trying to cultivate the garden God has given me. I've got my turf, and I'm trying to make something out of it. My performance matters to me, but I want it to matter most to you. You once were my cheerleader, are you still? I heard that every man does what he does for the admiration of one woman. You are that woman. I am hypersensitive to even the suggestion that I am a failure. Don't compare me to 'so and so,' who's ahead of everybody. Please be aware of saying I'm not good enough in my field. I feel driven to work and work hard. Please don't make that evil because it competes with family time. Help me with balancing the different parts of my life. I struggle with that. Don't make me second to the kids. I am not your helper. Let me know you are honored to be my helper, given to me by God. You did that in courtship and my heart was deeply touched. I could hardly wait to propose. Those feelings are still in me. Please don't see it as silly to admire me for my desire to succeed in my field."

**Practical
Application:**   Choose one and share what happened with the group:
* tell your husband "thanks" for working every day
* cheer his successes wherever they might be
* ask your husband to talk about his dreams like you
    did when you dated

Session 12. His Hierarchical Mind Set: Respecting His Desire to Protect, Provide, and Die for You.

As we just learned, God calls a husband to work in the field in order to provide for his family. This is his clear biblical responsibility: to provide and protect. He feels the call to oversee his family. Scripture sees it as positively fundamental. In his epistle to Timothy, the apostle Paul says, "But if

> " . . . the Lord God took the man and put him into the garden of Eden to cultivate it and keep it." – Genesis 2:15

anyone does not provide for his own, and especially for those of his household, he has denied the faith, and is worse than an unbeliever" (1 Timothy 5:8). But this concept goes even further. In the New Testament, the husband is called to be a Christ figure toward his wife: "For the husband is the head of the wife, as Christ also is the head of the church, He Himself being the Savior of the body" (Ephesians 5:23). So just as Christ died for the church, a husband sees himself as responsible to die for his wife. This means that he can and must "die" in myriad ways, large and small, over a lifetime, put-

> " . . . do not fear. I will do for you whatever you ask, . . . you are a woman of excellence." – Ruth 3:11

ting the needs of his wife and children ahead of himself.

But let's not forget that at the back of all of this is the very real notion that a man may be called to literally die for his family. How many fathers and husbands over the centuries and years were called to protect their families and countries in war? How many fathers and husbands forewent the luxuries of home life to risk life and limb on a cold, muddy battlefield? How many fathers and husbands today live with the very real knowledge that in the event of a war, or in some terrorist scenario, they would be called upon to risk their lives and comforts to protect their wives and children? Just because the last few decades have been relatively peaceful ones doesn't remove this threat from our lives and from the minds of many men.

And because this is at the back of many a man's mind, it seems only reasonable to him that his wife appreciate him and his willingness to do this.

> " . . . responsible . . . for their children."
> – 2 Corinthians 12:14

But how many wives ever really think about this? So when the husband feels himself to be the head or overseer, the one who chairs the marriage, he usually sees it as a duty, not as a right. He may not particularly like the role, but it's a role prescribed by God's Word. Another reality is that other men will invariably look down on him if he is irresponsible. So don't think your husband sees his role as a right. He probably sees it as a responsibility, one he may or may not be comfortable with, but a responsibility all the same.

Another reality for a man in this area is the fact that most wives expect their husbands to be primarily responsible. A husband who is dependent on a woman is uninviting to most women. She may well wonder whether he loves her for who she is or sees her as a meal ticket, an easy way out of his own duties and responsibilities. And if she is the provider and protector, she effectively now has a son, not a husband. That is repulsive to most women. So even though egalitarianism is espoused, in practical terms there cannot be two heads, even if a division of labor is sought. Fights over budgets happen in all institutions, and the institution of marriage is no different. But the buck has to stop somewhere. Even in secular marriages, if there is an honest stalemate, most wives are willing to defer and most husbands are willing to lead. The nature of women is deferential in the most positive sense of the word. This is a particular strength women have. Doing something in harmony is often more meaningful than whatever they ultimately choose to do. But a wife needs to feel her husband cares deeply about her needs and is putting her first, especially if his decision differs from what she might have wanted. This assumes a deep level of trust. If a wife fears neglect, she'll become aggressive or deceptive. A husband needs to feel his wife will follow instead of going behind his back. If a husband fears insurrection, he'll become either passive or domineering.

The problem today is that although a husband probably views his headship as a responsibility, a wife can see him as selfish. The Christian wife doesn't argue with what the Bible reveals, but she will contend with what she perceives to be a selfish or indifferent attitude in her husband. A wife yearns for her husband to be responsible, yet fears he will take advantage of her or neglect her. A wife can attack the headship teaching if the husband is too strong.

"You can't do that, we're equal!" She can attack him if he is too weak. "You aren't the spiritual leader!" Often a wife's reaction is rooted in her fears, but that doesn't mean that she longs for headship. Instead she fears that her husband might abuse his position to push his agenda. And so, over time, the husband no longer believes his wife wishes to honor him as the one who is primarily responsible. Though she expects him to be primarily responsible, he feels she sees him as irresponsible or sees him as a meal ticket. Many husbands do not see her fear, but instead feel she strikes out at him for reasons that do not seem reasonable to him.

Let's look at another example. Matt and Kelly are married, with three kids. As Christmas nears, Matt feels pressure to generate more money in order to pay for Christmas gifts. Kelly had complained at Thanksgiving, "I don't know how we're going to pay all of our bills plus get the kids what they are secretly hoping to receive. Your income just isn't there. I wish you would do more." Matt immediately volunteered for overtime at work. For three weeks in a row he didn't get home until after 10 p.m. He had to leave the house in the morning before 7 a.m. One evening Kelly breaks down crying. "You missed two of Bobby's basketball games, Susy was in the school play but you were absent, and Jeanne's home room is having a Holiday party for the parents but you're working." Matt gets mad. "Look, Kelly, I resent what you're saying. You expect me to work more and then criticize me for working too much. You hold me responsible and then tell me I'm irresponsible. Fine! Tomorrow, you go get a job!" Kelly is hurt. She blurts out, "You can't talk to me that way. You men are all alike; you think you have a God-given right to boss women around. You are so heartless!"

For as sensitive as women can be, Kelly is missing Matt's heart. The guy is trying his best but can't spin all the plates. He's trying to be reliable only to be told he is unreliable. He feels disrespected, and comes across even more unloving. He's not justified but we understand his vulnerability. Her reactions are not reasonable to him. Kelly has a good heart, but so does Matt. In today's marriages, though, empathy is usually extended to the wife. If the wife can make the case that her feelings are hurt and the kids are being neglected, then Matt is the bad guy. In this case, we can hear what happened next. It will be reported that Kelly was trying to get him to work less once she realized the family events were being missed by him. She will acknowledge she encouraged him to work more, but will contend that he should have backed off once it became apparent that wasn't working. It will be stated that Matt did not respond to her new request to work less. Instead, he argued, "I made a commitment to do overtime." It will be reported that Matt could have stopped working the overtime for the sake of the family, but he refused. His stated reasons (that they needed extra for Christmas and work schedules were already locked in) will not find much favor in light of Kelly's feelings about the family. At this point, Kelly will move into complaints, criticism, and even contempt. Matt will withdraw in anger. The Crazy Cycle will be launched, and it can seriously hurt the marriage.

So what's the answer? The key is to show respect to Matt for what he is seeking to do rather than send a message of disrespect for what she feels he is failing to do. If Kelly were to say, "Oh, Matt I feel horrible for complaining about not having enough money for Christmas. You are such a wonderful man and provider. You immediately acted on that request. I respect you so much. I am now feeling, though, that I put you in a position to miss the kids' activities. They look up to you and when you are present it means the world to them. Is there any way you could cut back on overtime? I know that may not be possible but if it is, your presence to the kids would make their day." A man will have a hard time resisting this. He'll do everything he can to change. If Matt keeps working because of his verbal commitments, and the kids express sadness over his absence, Kelly should let the children know that daddy is working extra because he wants this Christmas for them to be special. He is doing this for them in response to her request that he make extra money. The children might feel even more special! If a wife says, "Talking that way is stupid," she doesn't understand the male spirit nor her part in this dilemma.

A Word about the Word "Submission"

Few conflicts end in stalemate and few marriages demand that a wife win her disobedient husband without a word (1 Peter 3:1,2). But the daily ways a wife follows the clear teaching of the Bible on this unpopular topic of submission – a topic the evangelical wife sees staring her in the face – must still be done with a positive attitude and actions of unconditional respect. A wife can differ with her husband. She is not un-submissive when she differs. If she does it respectfully, she is submitting in the sense of submitting her negative emotions. She is bringing her negative, disrespectful reaction under control and replacing that with a positive, respectful attitude and action. When she does this, all will be okay if her husband is a man of good will. Sometimes she will defer to him, sometimes he will defer to her. In either case that is secondary to her putting on respect as an act of submission to his male need to feel respect during conflict.

Some wives get up in arms when a husband comes across as resisting her desires. He may not be resisting those desires at all. He may be resisting her contempt. But she may falsely conclude that the idea of submission is antiquated, since she loses on two fronts: she doesn't get her wishes and he is unkind in the process. To her, this submission thing doesn't work. What she fails to decode is her disrespectful tone, look, and words prompting his resistance. That's the killer. She doesn't see this because she feels she is full of love and he is unloving. Do you feel he never listens to your input? That may be untrue. He might be shutting down on your disrespectful way of delivering your information instead. Many wives are clueless on the negative, complaining, critical way they present their ideas. They feel they are just being themselves, and their husbands should accept it! Research has shown however, that husbands can interpret negative criticism as contempt for who they are as men. They withdraw. The wives then conclude they don't care and are selfish. That completely misses where men are coming from. This is next to impossible for a wife to believe since she would never stonewall like he does. For instance, a husband can come across as stubbornly selfish, not because he is being selfish, but he is provoked by what he feels is her disdain for him, so he stonewalls. By way of comparison, when you shut down on your husband when he makes a request with harshness, are you resisting his ideas or his unloving demeanor?

Oh, how this simple truth about submission being the positive application of respect has set Christian women free! This isn't about being a doormat, but being a woman of dignity, especially during marital conflict. God wants that for you, and you want that for yourself. It isn't easy but it certainly clarifies things, does it not? It isn't easy but it is a positive target at which you can take aim. This book gives you a ton of ammunition.

Submission never means submitting to evil. The first thing God did in the church was discipline a husband and wife, Ananias and Sapphira, for lying to the Holy Spirit. They died. The wife, Sapphira, was wrong for submitting to her husband's deception. She should not have submitted to that which was contrary to God (Acts 5:1f). Her submission to God should have taken precedence over her submission to her husband.

However, as the church submits to Christ's headship, so a wife should submit to her husband's headship (Ephesians 5:22; Colossians 3:18; 1 Peter 3:1; 1 Corinthians 11:3; Titus 2:5). What does this mean? The Greek word for submission is "hupotasso." Literally, it means to place under or rank under. In other words, a wife is called to come under the husband's umbrella of protection and provision. Because Paul and Peter both began their sections on marriage with submission (Ephesians 5:22 and 1 Peter 3:1) but ended with respect (Ephesians 5:33 and 1 Peter 3:2), then the first and foremost way a wife "submits" is by behaving respectfully, even if he is undeserving of respect. Peter clearly connects submission and respect in 1 Peter 2:18. "...be submissive...with all respect, not only to those who are good and gentle, but also to those who are unreasonable." Placing oneself under or ranking under with all respect is the call of God on a wife. I don't know why God instructs this; all I do know is that there cannot be two heads, and God has given the responsibility to the husband. The husband will be judged on whether or not he fulfilled his provider and protector role. If he is failing to be the kind of umbrella over her that he ought, Peter still calls wives to show a respectful attitude that says, "I am ranked under you as head."

A wife needs to go on record with her husband that she believes she is under his responsibility. She needs to respectfully express her commitment to place herself under him like a four-star general does toward a five star general. She must not assume he knows this unless she has verbally told him. He needs to hear from her that she is under him to be protected and provided for. If she fears saying this to her good-willed husband, she misses out on a tremendous way to relax him and energize him. Some conflicts continue between couples because the husband misinterprets his wife's heart. If a husband is not assured that his wife feels this way, he will read into her com-

plaints about money, insurance, retirement, medical coverage, reliable trans-
portation, alarm systems, etc. He will wonder if she is trying to make a point
about how lousy he is as a provider and protector. He is sensitive to this. She
needs to reassure him that she is expressing her fears. If she launches into
ways for him to be a better provider and protector, he can "hear" that to mean
she is the supervisor, and he is the employee. A wife can be full of love and
good intentions but come across to her husband as disrespectful. If a wife's
fears are so great that she fears letting her husband know she is ranked under
him, he'll continually see her as bossing him. She needs to verbalize her
commitment to the Word of God. She must not fear obeying God for fear her
husband will not be good, gentle, or reasonable enough.

Most wives expect husbands to be primarily responsible. Remember the
respect card? Write, "Thank you for feeling responsible to protect and provide, and even die for me. That makes me feel
secure." Sign it, "With all my respect, the one who
still admires you." Watch what he does in response!
One wife wrote, "I typed up a little card (had to

> ". . . fight for your . . .
> wives and your houses."
> – Nehemiah 4:14

add hearts to it) on the computer telling him how much I respect him for working so hard to provide for our family and letting me be a stay-at-home mom
for our three daughters. I then tucked it into his briefcase that was in his car
ready for work the next day. He found it mid-morning, [and] when he did he
called me and thanked me for making his WHOLE day. His last words before
hanging up were (as you said)...the predicted...I Love You...that was pretty fun
to see that this worked just as you had said it would." Respect ignites fond
feelings of love in his heart. If this wife voices a fear later on, this husband
will have on record what her deepest sentiments are.

What about mutual submission? Paul writes, "and be subject to one another in the fear of Christ" (Ephesians 5:21). The husband submits by putting
on an attitude of love, which is less natural. The wife submits by putting on an
attitude of respect, which is less natural. For a wife, showing respect is probably the most powerful way to demonstrate submission. Putting on respect
when she feels unloved means she is submitting to her husband. This has
eased many wives. The attitude of respect is the positive application of submission. Again, both Paul and Peter begin their sections with submission, but
end those sections with respect (Ephesians 5:33b; 1 Peter 3:2). Now, if there

is a stalemate decision that threatens the survival of the marriage, she is called by God to defer. But, day in and day out, most matters do not escalate to that level. Daily submission means showing an attitude of respect when persuading your husband he is wrong.

Why is her disrespectful attitude so threatening? Husbands have been designed by God with a hierarchical mindset. In other words, they are extremely sensitive to being put down as irresponsible. Dr. Deborah Tannen, a secular, feminist linguist, writes, "I now see that my husband was simply engaging the world in a way that many men do: as an individual in a hierarchical social order in which he was either one-up or one-down. In this world...people try to...protect themselves from others' attempts to put them down...." (*You Just Don't Understand - Women and Men in Conversation*. Publisher: Ballantine Books. pgs. 24,25). This hierarchical or headship orientation results in a husband being very sensitive to a "put down." In other words, he can feel put down when there is no disrespect intended. You may confront to clarify and connect, but he "sees" you confront to clobber and control. This is equivalent to a wife feeling unloved when a husband did not intend to be insensitive.

Reflection and Discussion:

Is your husband trying to say the following to you? Discuss why this is or is not his statement to you: "I prize you as first in importance. You are special to me. It is equally true that I see myself as first among equals. Is that special to you? God calls me to be the head. Let me know again that you see me this way and respect these desires. This to me is a responsibility, not a right. I don't expect you to bow to me. I don't think in those terms. It quenches me when some view men as high and mighty, when we feel it is our duty to die for you and the family. I am called to imitate Christ who is the head of the church. Don't put me down for feeling this way. Men feel the obligation to oversee. We're silent because certain voices scream at us that we see this as some divine right, not a divine responsibility. They scream that we will abuse women. But I am a good-willed man. You married me because you saw my heart. Don't lump me in with evil-hearted men. Don't belittle me. I am hypersensitive to the 'put-down.' Don't criticize me in front of others. My status in your eyes outweighs most things. Notice my promotions and rank in my field. If you confront me to connect, calm down and reassure me you aren't confronting me to control me. Look up to me. I'll melt. I don't believe there can be two heads. If there is a stalemate decision, threatening our marriage, let me know that you see me as primarily responsible. I need to feel this is your belief. My heart is touched."

Practical Application:

Choose one and share what happened with the group:

* say to your husband, "I really do look up to you for feeling responsible for me."

* tell him you're deeply touched by the thought that he'd die for you.

* praise his commitment to provide (bring home the bacon)

Session 13: His Authority: Respecting His Desire to Be Strong and Lead, and Make Decisions

What do you think of the following situation?

Shirley loves Steve to death. Not only is he a caring husband, he put her through grad school. They are excited about their first baby. She is due in three months. And Shirley looks forward to being home with her newborn child. Sometimes, though, she feels conflicted about staying at home while her husband provides. Shirley has her Ph.D. in Women's Studies, but was raised in a pretty traditional Baptist home. It's fair to say that she has some serious conflicts within herself on gender issues. When she decided to join a Bible study group – because she wanted to focus on her spiritual side – she was asked her opinion about respecting and submitting to husbands. The question set her off. "Frankly," she said, "too many women have been degraded through the centuries. I have no intention of having a collar and leash placed on me. I'm not some pet. I have brains. Steve and I are equal. If I don't want something, I veto it. Period. Just this week I told him he couldn't make a certain decision because we're equal. I will not endorse some old fashioned idea that women are puppets. Love is what matters. To me, to show respect somehow implies that the man is superior, and that kind of deference just sickens me. Men are arrogant. If they were more humble like most women, the world would be a wonderful place. I am into Jesus, who treasured women, not the male apostles who were chauvinistic. I am not inferior."

> "... act like men, be strong."
> – 1 Corinthians 16:13

Have you heard this someplace? Have you thought it yourself? Biblical teaching on authority, headship, and submission can create incredible tension and conflict for a wife. But usually this is not because of the teaching itself as much as it is because of a misunderstanding of the teaching. If a wife indeed views her husband as primarily "responsible" to protect and provide, and even die for her and the

> "... the contentions of a wife are a constant dripping."
> – Proverbs 19:13

children, she needs to understand the basics of Leadership 101, that a husband needs authority equal to his responsibilities. This is a law of leadership – in all leadership scenarios, not just marriage. If she holds him primarily responsible – and every woman we have met does – but exercises the ultimate authority with her veto power, he'll go through the roof. In business, if one is made primarily responsible to do something, one must be given the primary authority to do it. If this isn't the case, people will quit. If a board says to the CEO, "You are responsible for everything but have authority to do nothing," that person will resign. Nothing is worth that kind of frustration. So for a wife to hold her husband primarily responsible, but then grab the authority, is to trigger in the husband a desire to quit, move into passive irresponsibility, or ignore her when making decisions.

But a wife might rightly ask: "What if I am afraid of his intended decision?" If the husband is about to make a decision which the wife fears, the wife needs to express that fear. She shouldn't live in fear of a husband exercising his authority in their marriage. If she is worried about him investing $10,000 in a friend's golf shoe company, she needs to communicate those anxieties. But she must communicate respectfully. If she simply grabs the authority from the husband by saying, "You can't make that decision! We're equal!" it will provoke the husband. To a man this simply comes across as a challenge to his authority, and such challenges invariably backfire. So he'll do it anyway, or he'll shut down and become more and more passive.

Let's look at the Word of God on this topic. In 1 Timothy 2:12 we read, "But I do not allow a woman to...exercise authority over a man, but to remain quiet." These are chilling words to some women in our modern society. What can they possibly mean? The fact is that God's Word on this subject prevents a huge problem in marriage. God simply and straightforwardly asserts a husband's primary responsibility in marriages, and so He calls wives to express attitudes that communicate deference to that authority. He knows men, because he created them – He invented them. He knows how they tick. Wives might do well to heed Him on this prickly subject.

Sarah and I will never forget what one wife said at one of our conferences. She was making it clear that she understood Scripture on this subject and had no problem deferring to her husband. "I want him to lead," she declared. "I just want him to make the decision in accordance with what I want."

We thought she was joking, and laughed out loud, as did everybody else in the group. But the woman's face turned red. She'd meant it! Just as women have special insights into the nuances of love, and decry men's lack of insight on the subject, so many women can lack insight into the nuances of respect.

There is a real fear in some women about this subject. "If I let my husband make certain decisions," they say, "he'll make a bad decision!" Well, first of all, let's be very clear on this subject. Some decisions actually can have deeply harmful and lasting consequences, and no wife should remain silent if her husband is about to do something that may do terrible damage to the family. Indeed, there may come a moment in a marriage when a wife simply cannot go along with what her husband is proposing, and she may actually need to separate from him (1 Corinthians 7:11). Let's face it, if he has decided to sell the kids, you have no choice. But most conflicts are not nearly as black and white as that. Usually conflicts between husbands and wives are far more complicated and there is more gray than there is black or white (i.e. should we halt life support for our ninety-year-old grandfather?). Usually, you will consult with experts on these gray area issues.

Most real marital conflict is at the basic level of personal preferences, his versus yours. In this case, he wants to invest $10,000 in a friend's golf shoe company, and you oppose it, perhaps with good reasons. But you must realize that neither choice is evil. Neither is absolutely wrong, just different. People can and should be allowed to have different opinions, and even to make mistakes occasionally.

This does not mean neither person has strong convictions about his or her preference. We can have strong feelings about what we prefer. Read Romans 14. Sometimes our personal preferences can even be matters of conscience. During war time, we call certain people "conscientious objectors." In good conscience they cannot kill, so they serve in noncombatant arenas. Their decision is rooted in a Judeo-Christian worldview. Neither side is to pass judgment on the other as evil. Not wrong, just different. However, when it is a conflict over preferences or matters of conscience, you cannot say to your husband, "Thus saith the Lord you are wrong in the eyes of God for what you prefer! Your preference is sin because if I did this, I would be wrong in the eyes of God on this." Romans 14 teaches that just because that would be sinful to you, and thus sinful to God, does not mean it is sinful to your husband

and thus sinful to God. This is the point of Romans 14. We must live with the tension of differing preferences and convictions. We are not permitted to judge the other as sinful.

So, what should you do if he proceeds with what he prefers? As we have said, you certainly should voice your objections and thoughts, but you must do so respectfully. If there are eight solid reasons why investing $10,000 in a friend's golf shoe company is unwise, as his wife you are obligated to let him know those reasons, but you are also obligated to do so respectfully. If you have an MBA and accounting degree, don't throw this in his face. Use the wisdom those degrees have given you. Just be clear that your expertise and superior education on any subject do not give you the right to usurp your husband's authority. A husband is not an employee. A wife must also be careful never to communicate as a mother might with her son. This prohibition exists to protect their intimacy as husband and wife, which is her deepest value!

At this point comes the primeval scream of certain feminists! But some of these women don't understand what brings a good-willed husband under conviction. If a husband is wrong, showing contempt is not only unbecoming to a woman of God, it is ineffective. Yelling, "You can't do that, we're equal" won't work long-term in marriage. This violates Leadership 101, which says she cannot exercise the authority yet hold him primarily responsible as the spiritual leader. This sets him up for failure. This also runs contrary to her nature in that she doesn't want the ultimate authority anyway. I've not met a wife yet who wants her husband dependent on her. Though she can start ruling, that is not something she desires in her spirit. Her flesh can get the better of her, but in her deepest heart, ruling isn't energizing to her. She wants to be her husband's lover, not his mother.

"So what should I do if my husband is about to make a dumb decision? Should I simply say nothing and be a doormat?" Absolutely not, but the key is to respectfully go over the eight reasons – based on your skill and knowledge. First, hope that your husband hears you out and wisely heeds your sound and sage advice. And then, if he doesn't, hope he fails. That's right. Hope he fails. Why would we say such a thing? Because, if you are willing to let him lose ten thousand dollars – or whatever else is at stake, you will be allowing him to fail big and to learn once and for all, that your advice is nothing to sneeze at. Now, this is not so that you can say "I told you so!" On the contrary, it's to show him that he has a genuine treasure in you, one he would do well to prize. But he will only find out about who you are and your worth to him through your respectful behavior before and after his failure. His failure, large or small, awakens him to who you are!

"Well, okay," you ask. "What do I do after he fails?" You re-approach him on the heels of his failure saying with honor, "I still support and respect your desire to lead." Don't say any more. Leave the room. Go do something else. Never, ever say, "If you had listened to me in the first place, we wouldn't be in this pickle. I told you so." Avoid that like the plague. You might not realize it, but that is already ringing in his ears. He is anticipating you telling him this. This is why when you re-approach him respectfully, you blow him away. It is during this time period that your husband has his awakening to who you are. You can argue all day long that he should have known that already. He should have trusted you. He should have prized you. Etc. Etc. But if you act with honor, for most husbands, this first major failure shows him that you respect him for who he is regardless of his performance. And that is inestimably powerful. He thinks to himself, "Wow. She respected me before and she respected me afterwards. If I make another dumb decision, this is going to make it really hard for her to keep on respecting me." From that point on, when you respectfully come to him with a set of reasons about something, watch what happens. We predict he'll listen to you intensely and lovingly. Why? Because he sees you as an ally, not an enemy; as a partner, not as a competitor. He no longer feels he needs to prove himself to you. Yes, yes, he should have known that. However, without this kind of failure he won't feel it emotionally in his spirit. That's why his failure is to your advantage. It brings this home like nothing else. Further, when a new conflict arises, do the same thing again. Respectfully present your new set of reasons he should not do this. Let the truth of what you unfold carry its own weight. Have confidence in your content. Have confidence in your respect. The truth and respect will not only make you persuasive, they will ignite within the heart of this man a depth of love you didn't think possible.

How sad it is that many women simply dig their heels in and do battle. Or if they do give in, they do so with contempt, which prevents the husband from confessing his mistake and feeling fond feelings of love for his wife. For sure, if you come at him disrespectfully prior to the decision, he will defend himself. Afterwards, he will try to save face. It will be hard for him to admit defeat in the face of a contemptuous woman. The male nature finds that next to impossible, just as a wife finds it next to impossible to have sex with her harsh and angry husband. As lack of love crushes a wife, so lack of respect crushes a husband. Think about it.

And remember, his greatest need is for your admiration and respect. Through his failure he discovers that he *has* your respect. That respect is his to lose. That is key. His male logic kicks in. Most men are never the same again. If you want your husband to learn firsthand how wise and wonderful you are, understand why God does not instruct you to exercise authority over your husband. Having your respect is more important to him than having his way. He'll not ignore your counsel from that point on. He may not follow it, but you'll observe him become much more sensitive to your mind and heart when he differs.

Putting your own feelings as a wife aside for a moment, consider what studies have shown about men's leadership and authority around the world. The anthropologist Steven Goldberg, in preparing his study, *The Inevitability of Patriarchy*, examined most of the known anthropological and sociological literature and could find no society in which authority was associated chiefly with women in male-female relations. He found that instead, the degree to which women take power seems to depend on the extent to which the men are absent. No less an authority than Margaret Mead agreed with Goldberg's findings and went so far as to describe his presentation of the data as "faultless." In her review of Goldberg's study, she wrote, "It is true, as Professor Goldberg points out...Men have always been...the final authorities in the home." George Gilder in his book *Men and Marriage* also compared some 500 cultures and found that, in all of them, fighting and leadership were associated with the men.

In saying these things, we understand the anthropological reality on the subject, but what does Scripture say? It clearly implies that to be a man is to be strong: "...act like men, be strong" (1 Corinthians 16:13), and "Be strong, therefore, and show yourself a man" (1 Kings 2:2). It also implies that to be a husband is to manage: "if a man does not know how to manage his own household..." (1 Timothy 3:5) and "good managers" (1 Timothy 3:12).

In societies the world over, and in Scripture, it's clear that strength and leadership are fundamental to who a man sees himself to be. So if a wife puts her husband down for his weaknesses and his inept leadership, it can wound him horribly. And if that wife communicates that he can't do anything apart from her approval, his feelings of love for her can, and likely will, lessen.

> "It is better to live in a desert land Than with a contentious and vexing woman."
> – Proverbs 21:19

Angry Confrontations Backfire

Be careful about confronting your husband in anger. Through his blue lenses, he can feel you are confronting to control him, not negotiate with him. One man joked, "I hate to think my wife always gets her own way, but she writes in her diary a week ahead of time." In his book *The Stronger Sex*, Richard Driscoll cites the research of Dr. John Gottman: "The observation that women tend more toward angry confrontation has substantial support in marriage and relationship research. Women are seen to dominate in marital arguments about twice as often as men dominate... And in those most one-sided arguments where only one argues, by a ratio of six to one it is the women who demand and scold and the men who are scolded." (*Every Man: A Men's Journal*. August/September 2001, p. 19)

> ". . . under the authority of your husband, . . ."
> – Numbers 5:20

So if it is your desire that your husband be more responsible and exercise his authority in ways that are more loving to you, confront him respectfully. Actually say, "I don't want to be disrespectful. If you feel I am trying to dishonor you, please tell me. But I feel this decision isn't taking into account some key factors related to the family. When would you be available to talk about this?" If the husband is good-willed, and you speak respectfully as a woman of dignity, your husband will engage you. The bottom line is that you will either speak respectfully or disrespectfully, and disrespectful engagement will backfire on you. It's God who commands you to be respectful. If you are out of control in this area, your focus should properly be on your own lack of self-restraint, not your husband's poor leadership.

An additional point concerns negotiation among men. In the male arena, because a fight among men can be lethal, men approach issues in an analytical way with emotions controlled. If they lose control, or appear to be hyper-emotional, and speak words of dishonor, look out. This is taboo. Men have killed other men for this. Young men learn early about the honor code among men. Never, ever send a message of dishonor to a man unless you want to provoke him to fight or want him to be humiliated to run home to his mommy so all can laugh at him. In most cases, this corners the man and he must now fight. The conflict is escalated to dangerous levels.

Women among women, on the other hand, do not fear things rising to the level of violence. They can negatively vent and say nasty things but neither believes this is lethal. Consequently, women feel freer to verbally fuss and feud. To them scolding and finger pointing is not provocative. That never enters their mind. They are trying to resolve matters, not fight.

Imagine, though, what a husband feels as a man. If another man talked to him the way his wife sometimes talks to him, they'd get in a fistfight. It is obviously provocative. One man is not releasing his emotions to feel better, he is challenging him to a fight. He is not saying these things to resolve matters. This is why men avoid such language. This is why your husband exclaims, "Why are you provoking me? Why do you try to pick a fight with me?" You are in shock. What planet is he from? Yet, he is a normal male feeling that you are seeking to put him down, to corner him, to humiliate him. He, of course, is baffled as to why you are doing this. Confused, he exits and calms himself down. Later, he hears you judge him as unloving. The guy is totally confused. He feels himself trying to be loving, and he certainly isn't disrespectful like you, yet you are pouncing on him as a sad excuse for what it means to be a human being. If we don't think this dynamic is going on in evangelical homes, why are 5 out of 10 divorcing?

So, do your marriage a huge favor. If you want your negotiations to be calmer, understand how Blue sees things. Ask yourself the important Respect Question: "Is that which I am about to do or say going to result in my husband feeling respected or disrespected?" No matter how you speak, your husband might still get defensive and upset. That is not proof you are doing it wrong. If a husband claims you are disrespectful because you differ with him, then ask him: "Honey, can a wife show respect toward a husband yet disagree with him? How do you respectfully differ with your boss? Help me do this as you do this." Stay with it. Don't quit because it doesn't work the first several times. Will you still get hurt as a wife? Look, Emerson still hurts Sarah. She will confront him respectfully, but he can still get defensive and sarcastic, and we're the Love and Respect couple! Hang in there! Don't wimp out on this. God is for you, and He would not command you to do something that is designed to make you miserable. This is a fundamental principle and it works.

Reflection and Discussion:

Is your husband trying to say the following to you? Discuss why this is or is not his statement to you: "Believe in my desire to be a good leader. We both can't be the leader. I'm not asking you to agree with me on everything. And yes, we need to divide the labor based on our expertise, but what happens when we have an honest stalemate? I feel responsible before God. I feel I am going to be judged by Him for my leadership. Verbally recognize this. Also, do you realize I feel strong in relationship to your softness? Let me know you want to lean on my strengths. Tell me you need me. I'll serve you. Tell me you are in charge, and I'll compete or be apathetic. Can you see that my brawn and vigor exists to protect you? I'll use my powers to provide for you. Tell me you appreciate my good decisions – don't take them for granted. Don't focus on my weaknesses, but my strengths. Seek to be gentle in spirit though differing with my opinions. You won't lose power. Don't let fear control you. Don't listen to certain voices in your head about male authoritarianism. You married me because you saw me as good-willed. Express your longing to trust me. Don't put your heels in on every decision. Let me fail. Don't say you want me to be the leader, but then tell me I can't do something if it isn't in keeping with what you want. Respectfully point out my irresponsible behaviors, but don't communicate that I am impotent and weak. Don't rob me of my authority by your veto. Don't go behind my back. Don't create mutiny in the family. Don't tell me I am responsible for everything but have authority to do nothing. Don't try to control me by saying, "You can't do that, we're equal." I need to know you want to follow me. I need to be needed by you. This ignites fond feelings of love in my heart for you."

Practical Application:

Choose one and share what happened with the group:
* tell your husband he is strong and you need him
* praise his good decisions
* honor his authority in front of the kids and differ with him in private

Session 14. His Insight: Respecting His Desire to Analyze and Counsel

Veronica's dad made very good money. Growing up she had her own credit card. Now as a married, career woman, Veronica felt she had a right to spend money on things she needed and wanted. As a couple, she and her hus-

> "The woman of folly is boisterous; She is naïve and knows nothing."
> — Proverbs 9:13

band Daryl were not on welfare. But the debt load from the home and cars, and $18,000 on credit cards, half of which was for Veronica's clothing, finally pushed a button in Daryl. "Veronica," he told her, "we've talked three times about this in the last eight weeks. Why are you ignoring me? This is horrible

stewardship. I am telling you, we need to budget things and stay on budget." She flippantly replied, "I have a right to spend money, and it's no big deal. We both have jobs and we can pay it back. You're such a worry wart. You don't know what you're talking about." Uncharacteristically, Daryl harshly says, "You are clueless on saving money." He throws his checkbook against the wall.

When a husband feels disrespected, he can react without love. A husband can deflate when his wife treats him as though he has no knowledge and good counsel. He gets angry and then withdraws. He can become very discouraged when he is trying to be helpful and solve a concern.

A common expression some wives use is, "Don't try to fix me." But let

> "Then Elkanah her husband said to her, 'Hannah, why do you weep and why do you not eat and why is your heart sad? Am I not better to you than ten sons?'"
> — 1 Samuel 1:8

me share why men are solution-oriented. Men generally score higher on math and analytical tests. Women generally score higher on the verbal. Consequently, in marriage husbands tend to be more solution-oriented. Interestingly, when one man approaches another man with a problem, both instinctively know why. Men tend to think about their problems first, and if solved, there is no point in talking. If though, my best male friend approaches me with a problem, we recognize that he has thought about it as far as he can but couldn't find a solution. He is now coming to me for a solution. I start throwing out solutions to remedy the problem. I am seeking to be helpful because I care. Yet, when a wife approaches a husband with a problem and he tries to solve it, she may scream, "Quit trying to fix me! You're so uncaring!"

Too many husbands have told us, "If I say something, I'm in trouble, and if I don't say something, I'm in trouble. But, if I don't say something, I am in less trouble." How many Christian wives are crying out for their husbands to be spiritual leaders, but if these men contribute truth to them as they would with their best male friend, the wives are offended?

Deborah Tannen, in *Talking from 9 to 5,* has found that when conflict happens, women tend to take it more personally than men do (pgs 57-63). In other words, similar conflicts among men are not personalized like this. In marriage, a husband can speak his mind in a way that he feels is helpful. Yet, his wife personalizes this to such an extent that she yells and starts questioning, which now leads to an hour-long discussion: What did he mean? Why did he say what he did? Can he understand where she's coming from? In the future, can this be approached differently? Sometimes this kind of questioning is okay, but other times, some of a husband's comments, though, are stated in a straightforward conversation with no ill will or anger. At those moments a wife needs to pull back. Over the years, we have seen women read meaning into comments that is not there. Her husband is offering good insight, but this is interpreted as a put down. "You know, one way to balance the check book is by using this new program I just found." She reacts, "What are you saying? Because I made several mistakes, you feel I am stupid, don't you. You feel I can't do anything. Here, you take over my check book since you're so high and mighty."

Husbands do not have as much insight into the subtleties of love as wives, but God has clearly revealed that wives need their husbands. Wives can be deceived. We read in I Timothy 2:14, "it was not Adam who was deceived, but the woman being quite deceived, fell into transgression." Then again in 2 Corinthians 11:3, "But I am afraid, lest as the serpent deceived Eve by his craftiness..." Some women can be "led on my various impulses" (2 Timothy 3:6). Modern thinking has advocated that men listen to their wives' intuition

"Then to Adam He said, 'Because you have listened to the voice of your wife, . . .'" – Genesis 3:17

"But his wife, from behind him, looked back, and she became a pillar of salt." Genesis 19:26
"Remember Lot's wife." – Luke 17:32

to such an extent that the suggestion that wives can be deceived is politically incorrect. We certainly do not seem concerned that wives can mislead husbands. Have we swung too far?

A husband had an opportunity to move from Nashville to Texas for more money. But he did not want to leave Nashville. His wife wanted to go to Texas. She was raised there, there was more money, and her dad was a pastor in Nashville, but they had left his church so leaving Nashville would lessen her pain. But the husband did not believe it was right to go to Texas. A year later that business group in Texas folded. So, it isn't always the idea that if a wife has a good feel about something that it is a wise thing to do. She can fail to have discernment. She can let her own "relational" concerns drive a decision. Years ago we would have urged the husband to listen to his wife. We had tipped too far in favor of woman's intuition.

Why are some wives so down on men? Rooted in an evolutionary worldview, feminism teaches that women have evolved to a higher level and are better. Men need to change and catch up. This has spilled over into the church. Women are viewed as more righteous, even though some have become self-righteous. This is reflected in wives confessing their desire to change their husbands, saying, "I have to stop trying to be my husband's Holy Spirit." There is no vacancy in the Trinity.

Men can be viewed as unrighteous because they struggle with issues that women do not. Husbands struggle with sexual temptations, anger and violence, and being less nurturing. To wives, these can threaten love in a colossal way. Some wives have contempt for men who struggle with lust, losing their cool, or overlooking family concerns. But wives can be deceived in that they do not see that they are depriving their husbands sexually (1 Corinthians 7:5), provoking them with their contempt (2 Samuel 6:16f), and expecting too much due to their own discontent (Genesis 3:6). Also, wives can be blind to the fears that control them, which is a sin (Isaiah 19:16; 1 John 4:18). Vicious, verbal attacks during PMS are sins (Proverbs 21:19; Galatians 5:20). Eating problems can be sins (Proverbs 23:20), as can taking into account his offenses

> "If . . . the wife you cherish, . . . entice you secretly, saying, 'Let us go and serve other gods' . . ."
> – Deuteronomy 13:6

> "He who covers a transgression seeks love, but he who repeats a matter separates intimate friends."
> – Proverbs 17:9

(1 Corinthians 13:5). Gossip is a sin (1 Timothy 3:11; 5:13; Titus 2:3). This is not to shame wives but to appeal to them to extend more mercy and honor to their husbands.

The point for the Christian wife is to understand that BOTH men and women need the Savior. "For all have sinned and fall short of the glory of God" (Romans 3:23). Our sins can be different, but sin is still sin. How easy, though, to judge another where we are strong. Women typically don't struggle with lust, violence, and overlooking family concerns in order to succeed in the field. If that becomes the criteria for wholeness, men are dead in the water.

Respecting him means appreciating his desire to analyze and counsel. Though she has intuition and insight, he too has wisdom and shrewdness. Though Adam disobeyed, Eve was deceived. She listened to voices that played on her dissatisfactions. Eve had Paradise but wanted more. She did not listen to Adam. A wife can expect perfection. She can develop an attitude that says, "Listen to my voice. Change!" Motivated by the impulses of love, she can rationalize her contempt. She can dismiss her husband's solutions by labeling him un-empathetic.

He may not be as insightful as you want, but focus on his desires and strengths. Sarah met with a group of high school girls. She asked, "What do

> "To the pure, all things are pure; but to those who are defiled and unbelieving, nothing is pure, . . ." – Titus 1:15

you like about women and dislike about men? List them out." When they discussed the differences, the negative energy in the room toward the men went through the roof, but the positive energy about women was incredible. The women could do no wrong. The next week she had them list out all the things about men they liked, and the things about women they disliked, and there was a complete reversal. The positive energy toward the men went through the roof, and the disdain for some women was a bit alarming. Then Sarah told these young women to learn a lesson. What you focus on in another person will determine to a great extent what you feel about him. Irving Becker wrote, "If you don't like someone, the way he holds his spoon will make you furious; if you do like him, he can turn his plate over into your lap and you won't mind."

Certainly men are created in the Image of God as are women, so to buy into the notion that husbands are worse sinners, needing the Savior more than women, is heresy. In fact, when was the last time you heard this preached: "For a man...is the image and glory of God; but the woman is the glory of man" (1 Corinthians 11:7)? The bottom line is, he needs to feel that she desires to bring him honor. One young girl admitted to Sarah that during the first week, she felt women were the better species but the second week realized one isn't better than the other, just different.

If you want to motivate your husband to feel more love for you, why not honor his desire to be insightful? If you are burdened about something and he starts to give you a solution, you might say, "I respect your desire to help me. What could help me most right now is your understanding. I need a listening ear. Is this a good time to talk?" Such a statement works, but because the words respect and strength are used, some wives won't state it like this. Instead they'll say, "Look, I need to talk and you need to listen."

Reflection and Discussion:

> Is your husband trying to say the following to you? Discuss why this is or is not his statement to you:
> "I like fixing things. I do this because I feel I know how to do certain things. I have experience. When I hear a problem, I want to solve it. I am analytical. Can you praise me for this bent? I know you want me to listen, and I am learning. But please esteem me for my attempt to be a man of integrity. By that I mean not all of your feelings should be validated. Not all of your feelings are valid. Because you feel something, doesn't make it true. If I disagree, don't complain that I am without understanding and empathy. Honor me for caring enough to differ. I really want to help. Appreciate my struggle. At times you want me to say nothing, yet when I say nothing you are upset with me. You want me to talk, yet when I talk you are upset with me.

Don't berate me for not intuitively sensing when to listen and when to speak. I am not a woman. Tell me I am a caring and insightful person even though I am not as expressive and responsive as you. Tell me you need my objectivity and factual qualities. Appreciate my logic. Seek my advice. Tell a group of people how insightful I was on something, and my feelings of love for you intensify."

Practical Application:

Choose one and share what happened with the group:
* thank your husband for his advice and appreciate his knowledge
* let him fix things and applaud his solution orientation
* tell him up-front that you need a listening ear, and not a solution

Session 15. His Relationship: Respecting His Desire for a Shoulder-to-Shoulder Friendship

In front of Stu, Missy told the marriage counselor, "I don't accept Stu's stupid invitations. He used to say, 'Let's go to the athletic club to jog and lift weights together.' Or, he'd say, 'Hey, let's watch TV together.' Or, 'Let's join that six week volleyball class.' Or, 'I bought

> "Then the Lord God said, 'It is not good for the man to be alone; I will make him a helper suitable for him.'" – Genesis 2:18

a tandem bike.' But all of this is about him. He is so self-centered. We need to talk if our relationship is going to make it. Communication is the key. I want to work on the relationship, but he wants to play."

A husband can deflate when feeling his wife is suggesting he is unlikable, lacks the desire for closeness, fails as a romantic companion, and is an uncommunicative, bad listener.

A wife can so focus on face-to-face talking that she overlooks the massive amount of positive energy that fills his spirit when she does shoulder-to-shoulder activities. In fact, he has the same goal that she does: to be close friends. He feels respected when you appreciate his shoulder-to-shoulder friendship. Again, in Titus 2:3,4 we read, "Older women...that they may encourage the young women to love (phileo) their husbands." Notice that the Greek word for love is phileo. This is the root of the name Philadelphia, city of brotherly love. In other words, in the home, a wife and mother can become unfriendly. She loves her family with agape-love, but she is extremely negative. Her negativity pushes the husband away. He doesn't want to sit down and talk with her face to face. In marriage, there is to be lover friendship. In the Song of Solomon we read God's words, "friends... O lovers" (5:1). God Himself wants them to be friends. Later the wife says, "he is wholly desirable. This is my beloved and this is my friend..." (5:16). A husband seeks that, but pursues it by requesting shoulder-to-shoulder activities. He wants her to be friends with him again as they were in courtship. He wants to do again what they did in courtship. Whereas a wife recalls the face-to-face talking, he recalls the way she watched him from the stands play basketball, or watched a sporting event with him, or joined him in the garage as he worked on a project.

In her book, *Gender and Discourse*, Deborah Tannen revealed research that was surprising. By way of background, she selected four age groups of males and females. Two boys and two girls from second grade, two boys and two girls from sixth grade, two boys and two girls from tenth grade, and two men and two women who were twenty-five years of age. First, each pair was to come into a room. They were to sit in that room, just the two of them, and talk. In that room were two chairs.

She found that males and females reacted differently to that situation. In order to talk, all the females either turned in their chairs to face each other and leaned forward to talk, or turned their chairs toward each other to talk. The males, on the other hand, sat in the chairs facing out, shoulder-to-shoulder. They did not turn the chairs, nor turn in their chairs to face each other. Periodically, they turned their heads toward one another but generally talked looking straight ahead.

Second, the conversations were video taped and recorded. By doing this, Tannen sought to answer the question, who had the most intimate conversations? Most would conclude that the women had the most intimate of conversations. Is not the assumption that intimate conversation cannot happen apart from close, face-to-face verbal interaction? What Dr. Tannen found was surprising:

"The conversation of the tenth-grade boys provides dramatic evidence that physical alignment away from rather than toward each other does not mean lack of engagement. As described above, the tenth-grade boys sat parallel to each other, stretched out in postures that could be interpreted as lackadaisical and careless, in one case, occasionally, and in the other case, almost never glancing at the other. Viewing the videotape with the sound turned off could easily give the impression that these boys are disengaged. But turning the sound up reveals the most 'intimate' talk heard in any of the tapes I observed" (p.96). Dear wife, make the choice to be with your husband, shoulder-to-shoulder, doing activities. Eventually he'll talk intimately with you–if he feels you like him.

Did you know some suggest boys not enter school until age ten? Little boys learn best outside, doing activities, and listening to stories. But what do we do? We bring them inside and make them sit still in order to learn abstract concepts. It has been said, "God speaks to little boys when they're fishing." Jesus was the Master teacher. He and his twelve disciples spent most of their time outside, doing activities, and telling stories (parables). Jesus understood men. A Christ-like wife, one seeking to have "the mind of Christ," will too (1 Corinthians 2:16).

A fellow was making a porch. He called his wife to come out to be with him. She came out and started talking. He said, "I don't want to talk; I just want you out here with me." She said, "You've got to want to talk. That's why you called me out here." He said, "I don't gotta wanna talk, I just want you with me." They got in a big fight and she walked off. A little while later, he got lonely and wanted her out there, so she rejoined him. But within five minutes, she started talking. He said, "I just want you with me. I don't want to talk." She was in disbelief and exited. Months later, they attended a Love and Respect Conference. They learned that he could be filled with positive energy by her shoulder-to-shoulder presence without her talking. A week or so later, he was painting. Out of the corner of his eye, he saw her coming toward him with a patio lounge chair. She laid back and just watched him. She had no book or project; she just watched him, without critiquing him, "You missed a spot over there!" What they experienced was incredible. He was so blessed in his heart. He said, "It just made me feel so good." She said to him, "This is what you want, isn't it?" He replied, "Yes, it is."

Emerson recalls growing up in a blue-collar area, seeing men outside, working under their cars: "As I rode my bike by their houses, I saw a wife here and there sitting on a bar stool next to the car. His feet were sticking out and she sat there on the stool, chewing gum, doing her nails, and a few were smoking cigarettes. As I reflected, there wasn't much talking between the two of them, yet it dawned on me that those marriages lasted. I then remembered there was no jack holding up that car. It was resting on his chest! He was so energized and strengthened by her presence, he didn't need a jack!"

Reflection and Discussion:

> Is your husband trying to say the following to you?
> Discuss why this is or is not his statement to you:
> "I need you to be my friend and companion, even my

buddy. During courtship, you could hardly wait to be with me because you liked me. Please be more friendly toward me in the home. I feel you scold me. I need a lover, not a mother. I want you to see me as your ally, not your enemy. I like it when you want to be at my side. I like it when you want to be with me 'just because.' I like it when you want to watch me do something – without critique. I want you to be with me at times without talking. I want you to like me, not just love me. I want to be close to you shoulder-to-shoulder. I like being alone and in solitude but knowing you are in the next room.   Please don't view me as the "tin man" who has no heart. Don't pass judgment on the quality of my friendships because I don't relate with my guy friends in the same way you relate with your girlfriends. I would die for some of my buddies. Would you die for your girlfriends? When we greet one another in the evening, will you do so positively? Can you hold off the complaints of the day, and when I leave in the morning, would you express something positive to me? I married you because I needed your positive companionship. I want you to be my friend. Oh, this creates such deep feelings in my heart toward you."

Practical Application:

Choose one and share what happened with the group:

* tell your husband you like him, or tell him certain things you like about him
* do recreational activities with him or watch him do them
* encourage alone time for your husband; this energizes him to reconnect later on

Session 16. His Sexuality: Respecting His Desire For Sexual Intimacy

Did you know that a husband can deflate when feeling his wife is suggesting he is oversexed, unworthy of a sexual response, or to be rewarded if he is good? A man thinks in terms of sexuality differently than his wife, and so he is particularly sensitive to put-downs in this realm.

Early on in many marriages, a husband sees his wife as his best friend and confidante. How sad that changes – but it doesn't have to. You need to begin to work on this, to encourage him to open up to you about whatever is on his mind. Here's a cautionary example to think about.

One day at work, a woman goes to the drinking fountain at the same time that a man does. Having no bra on, she bends over, giving him an eyeful. He can't believe his eyes. That night, he shares with his wife what happened and how it tempted him. His wife goes ballistic. "How dare you look at another woman? You've been spending time with her, talking and touching, haven't you? You are lying!"

Because of the way female sexuality is different from male sexuality, the wife got the whole thing wrong. Men are intensely visually wired. They are generally aroused by what they see. But of course, female sexuality is entirely different. Most women experience no arousal apart from time together, lots of talking, and meaningful touching. So, when her husband suggested that he was aroused, she projected onto him her female sexuality and assumed he was nursing a deep friendship. She was threatened, and reacted.

And of course that's a pity, because as soon as she did, her husband decided that was the last time he'd share his feelings in this area with his wife. Most husbands want to be open with their wives on this subject, but a wife's critical comments can put a quick end to that. A wife naturally desires her husband to be open about things that result in the feeling of love. "I want you to make me feel good by talking to me about things that I value," you might think. "Don't tell me the struggles of your soul if they threaten me. And then, let me criticize you for never being open with me." But you've got to reverse course on this, or you'll hurt the communication between you and your husband badly.

If you shame your husband for revealing his sexual temptations, he'll almost certainly clam up on the subject for good. He loses face and respect. Since respect is a huge value, he won't subject himself to this humiliation again. He feels scolded by his second mother. The message you are sending is: "If you love me, you won't have these feelings. So, don't you dare feel this way, and don't ever bring this up again." So, he doesn't. Even more painful to him is your request that he have eyes only for you but when he does, you tell him to get away. In fact, you may say, "Is that all you ever think about?"

Similarly, most husbands feel uncomfortable sharing their desire for sex with their wives because their wives find it somehow upsetting. What a pity! Look at it this way, a husband needs sexual release in the same way that you need emotional release. And remember that God made him that way, just as he made you the way you are. What would it be like for you if your husband said, "I can't talk, I have a headache." What if your husband did not talk to you for three days, three weeks, or three months? Your husband needs sexual release like you need emotional release. If you were given large doses of testosterone, you'd understand. Of course this is not to justify inappropriate male lust. Jesus is clear on that subject. But the Bible also says, "stop depriving" (1 Corinthians 7:5) and "let her breasts satisfy you at all times" (Proverbs 5:19). Sexual pleasure and fulfillment are not wrong; they are ordained by God, specifically for marriage. Men naturally have a strong desire that needs to be satisfied (1Corinthians 7:9). Think about this biblically, not carnally. It will make a big difference in your marriage.

> "Let the husband fulfill his duty to his wife, and likewise also the wife to her husband."
> – 1 Corinthians 7:3

> "The wife does not have authority over her own body, but the husband does; and likewise also the husband does not have authority over his own body, but the wife does." – 1 Corinthians 7:4

"But he needs to talk to me first," some wives will say, "then I'll respond." One woman took this position for years. Then God placed it on her heart to first reach out to her husband sexually. As she did this she noticed that he started talking afterwards. She discovered that she reached his spirit through the sexual. Enabling him to release his sexual tension and desire, freed him up in his spirit. She didn't understand this but recognized it was true. We urge the same thing of husbands, as well. Many men cannot comprehend how a woman needs to talk to release her emotions, but the women expect the men to understand and respond. Is it not fair then for a husband to expect his wife to understand his needs?

> "I am my beloved's, And his desire is for me."
> – Solomon 7:10

Reflection and Discussion:

Is your husband trying to say the following to you? Discuss why this is or is not his statement to you: "I need to be sexually intimate with you. I feel awkward talking about this. I am very vulnerable in this arena. I know you are tired. I know the kids are important. I know you don't always need or want to be sexually intimate. But I am your husband. Do I matter? As you have a need to talk, which to you is the loving thing to do, I have a need for sex, which honors me. Punishing me dishonors me. Depriving me angers me, and subjects me to temptations. I wish I was not this way. I know you feel I need you for only one thing. But empathize with my maleness and my visual orientation (MAT 5:28). All the young men in our extended families are the same. Be understanding about how self-conscious I am sexually. Pick up on my sexual hints. I express them indirectly to protect myself from your rejection. I am different from you, but am I wrong? Please don't make me feel abnormal compared to you. I need you. In telling me to have eyes only for you, don't push me away. Tell me you understand my needs and temptations, and watch my heart leap out of my chest for you."

Some couples experience intense tension on this front. We have encouraged some wives to respond to their husbands on a regular or predictable schedule to remove the guesswork. It may not sound romantic but actually increases the romance. In most cases, wives want sex less than the husbands. The wives want affection without it always leading to sex. Husbands, though, are uncertain if "this time" it might lead to something. So, the husbands tend to push, especially if there is never any indication when such sexual intimacy will happen. To remove that aggression and uncertainty, some couples introduce set times for sex. It actually creates romance, because the husband knows the other times are for pure affection and closeness without sexual results. One wife balked at this when we shared this idea. She later wrote, "Just to let you know – the suggestion you gave of setting aside regular time for being intimate so that we could be close at other times without pressure is working very well. It has really taken the 'edge' off of our relationship." Before you laugh, try it for six weeks. And if you flat-out reject your husband until you are interested, please meditate on 1 Corinthians 7:5, "Stop depriving one another, except by agreement for a time that you may devote yourselves to prayer, and come together again lest Satan tempt you because of your lack of self-control."

Practical Application:

> Choose one and share what happened,
> if appropriate:
> * initiate with your husband periodically
> * respond more often and regularly
> * let him share his sexual temptations without
>   shaming him

Session 17: The 14-Day Plan
(Note: Please start this two weeks before this session)

If you are thumbing through this book and your eyes land on this part first, "The Respect Plan," please favor yourself and start at the beginning! You may not appreciate, and may well

> "Prepare plans by consultation, . . ."
> – Proverbs 20:18

even mock, the information below. That is because you are very likely a contemporary woman who has been conditioned by our culture, and much of what you've learned will not allow you to accept any of this apart from the rationale set forth in book one.

Earlier, we made the case that you may feel unloved by your husband. The simple reason for that may be due to your husband not feeling respected. Right or wrong, that's how he feels. Consequently, he has pulled back from you, and comes across even more unlovingly. The fact is, he loves you and knows you love him. He is a bit angry and silent due to the feeling that you do not like who he is as a human being. Your defensive reaction to his failure to love you feels offensive to him. He deals with that in ways that you feel are even more unloving. Yet, he has basic good will. He simply does not know how to respond lovingly when feeling a woman has contempt in her heart for who he is as a man. You take your negative reactions more lightly, and because he goes silent you interpret that as unloving, not as his attempt to do the honorable thing and keep himself calm.

If you need him emotionally – even more than he needs you – you have to make a decision. Will you resist what is being said because it is unfair, or will you enter into this plan because you want to introduce a positive change in your marriage? We know you feel that your love for him should be enough to motivate him to love you. But is it working? Is your disrespect making a larger withdrawal than the deposit your love makes?

Our position is that your focus needs to shift from love to respect. If you are coming across disrespectfully while trying to love him, not only does that de-motivate your husband to love you, he does not value your love as much as he ought to. You can argue until you are blue in the face that your husband shouldn't feel this way. You can argue he started the marital problems by his unloving demeanor. You can argue, and rightly so, that he is completely mis-interpreting you. Even so, that won't rejuvenate his feelings of love in your marriage. Maybe it should, but it won't. Blame placing doesn't motivate anyone. And what makes this even more frustrating is that your disrespect definitely does not motivate him to be loving! Now, in a woman's world, all this discussion on respect would be a moot point. Two women would instinc-tively know verbal explosions lead to resolution and reconciliation. The goal is not humiliation of the other but harmony. After the negativity was released and tears were shed, hugs would be given, forgiveness extended, laughter would re-enter, and you would move on. Men don't have these verbal exchanges, however, because it could lead to a fist-fight. Rather, men go silent, allow the other to calm down, and drop the subject and forget about it. This is the hon-orable thing. But two women rarely resolve conflict this way! So imagine what happens when he does the honorable thing from his view by going silent, but to him you do the dishonorable thing by verbally criticizing. Imagine what happens when you do the loving thing from your view by demanding that he talk, and he does the unloving thing by refusing to talk!

"But I love him, why won't he change? Why won't he move first?" Well, he is moving first by doing the honorable thing. He knows you love him. That's not his struggle. He struggles with the feeling that you do not like him. If your husband does not feel you respect him, he will not have fond feelings of love for you. Sadly, many wives readily confess, "I don't like him nor respect him. I love him, but there are things about him that make me spitting mad." That attitude shuts a man down. The only way to re-open him is to come across to him in a way that results in him feeling you like and respect him. Of course, this is the problem. These wives shout, "He doesn't deserve my respect. No way am I going to do this. That would be hypocritical. I feel no respect." That is why we preach unconditional respect. If you are the mature one and act on this respect plan, you can create changes. It is a law of love and respect; when one spouse changes, the other spouse changes. In your case, when you as a wife change by showing unconditional respect, your hus-band will change by showing love. You don't do it for that reason, but when you do this, the results are probable. If a wife refuses to be unconditionally respectful – and she can come up with a dozen reasons why she should not – it is unlikely the husband will be more loving. If she stubbornly refuses, which some women do primarily because of disgust and resentment, she forfeits her influence on his heart.

For those of you ready to do the plan, it will be for fourteen days. The challenge is to go two weeks doing these activities, and do so without showing disrespect to your husband. This is a two-week fast from negative criticism of who he is. Can you do it? Will you try? Remember, some Christians have been persecuted and gone to their deaths as martyrs still saying, "Father, forgive them, they know not what they do." Is it too much to challenge you to go two weeks showing respect to your husband who is good-willed, not an evil enemy?

In doing this plan, you will be acting on the will and word of God. You will declare that you trust God. You are doing this from a heart that loves and reverences God. The reason it may

> "The plans of the diligent lead surely to advantage..."
> – Proverbs 21:5

not have worked in the past is that you didn't understand the importance of unconditional respect. As a technique, you may have tried it, but when it didn't work, you returned to your old way of reacting. The truth is, though, that this is God's call on your life whether it works or not. The Bible commands you to be a respectful woman (Ephesians 5:33; I Peter 3:1,2). As your husband is called to love, you are called to respect. That your husband has been preached at to love is obvious. Every pastor, writer, and radio host has told him this. What no one has pointed out in depth is what "causes" him to come across in an unloving manner on many occasions: your disrespect. Further, who has suggested he may not be unloving at all? He may be doing the honorable thing when he goes quiet as a way of loving God and honoring the marriage, by preventing things from exploding. Who has made the case that your unconditional respect, not your love, is what best motivates him to be more expressive of his love? Well, you get the point. The encouraging thing is that when you do this toward a good-willed husband, he typically "changes" for the better. For two weeks, though, will you do this whether he responds or not? Will you do this as an act of obedience to God?

Fast from complaints and criticisms for these fourteen days. Bite your tongue. We're talking two weeks. Do you want to look back in thirty years and wonder why you wimped out? You need to go through this. If you cannot be respectful in obedience to Scripture, do you have a right to expect your husband to be loving in obedience to Scripture? Let God favor you (1 Peter 2:19,20). We believe you will notice a change in your good-willed husband.

As you read on, some will say, "no way." Do you know why? Some don't want this positive change in their marriages. If their husbands become more loving, they will have to maintain a respectful approach. Despite their complaints, these women have settled into a life-style of feeling sorry for themselves, being negative and angry, and soliciting empathy from their girlfriends. They've taken the path of least resistance. Regardless of what they say, they don't want their marriages to change. They want their husbands to change while they remain the same critical women. What this plan will reveal is that they like the victim role. On the other hand, there are women who want to motivate their husbands God's way. They have the proper attitude and maturity to act on this. They have an active faith in Jesus. If their husbands are good-willed, the results will be positive, if not amazing.

DAY 1. When your husband comes home this evening, smile and tell him you are glad he is home (2 Corinthians 13:12). Go to him and greet him, like you did when courting. If you have not done this for a while, he will look at you with a look that says, "What's going on here?" Just ignore it and head into the kitchen or wherever. Don't hang around long enough to start talking. Get on with some task. Don't take up offense over his sarcasm if he adds, "What are you up to?" The contrast may be so startling, what do you expect him to say? Many men react this way. They like what just happened, but it is so striking compared to the routine, they tease with mockery. Let that roll off your beautiful back. Some wives become too familiar with their husbands, so immediately they blurt out a negative reaction, "Well, so much for that 14-Day Respect Plan! This won't work with you!" Some of you talk way too much! Quiet down, please. What kind of wisdom is this? Are you only doing this so you can justify quitting? Do you want to sabotage this in the first minute? You can if you want. You have the power. For those of you sincere about this, though, be prepared for him to follow you. He may ask, "Why did you greet me that way?" Just say, "I feel I am usually too preoccupied when you come home. Today, I wanted to welcome you home. I hope that's okay." Move out of the room to another task. For those of you who fear this will lead to sex, don't conclude this. If he jokes with you about sex, just say, "It isn't about sex; I just feel you deserve a more positive greeting, and I wanted to greet you today. I hope it encouraged you." Go to another room. Don't get into any conversations if you are going to complain about something. That is taboo! Your goal is to be positive, get to the point, and move on.

DAY 2. The next night greet him with a hug (1 Thessalonians 5:26). Remember, what you feel is secondary. This is an act of obedience to God. Again, a husband may call attention to what you're doing. He is apt to say, "Wow, two days in a row. What do you want, money?" Just ignore it. Don't be intimidated by a little sarcasm. You're tougher than that, especially if we tell you ahead of time it is coming. He is doing this because what you are doing feels good to him. What is sarcasm to you is playful bantering to him. After you hug him, go onto some task in another room. This is not done to get him to talk, though you may notice him moving toward you. That means it is already working. At this point though, keep moving away from him. Go to another room. We are not playing a game here, but trying to avoid premature talking about unresolved stuff. His responsiveness may be the kind of thing you look for in order to surface "problems" between you. "Ah, he is receptive." At this juncture, don't do that. This is a fast for two weeks from complaints. Plan the respect, and respect the plan!

DAY 3. Tonight, make his favorite dessert or meal (Proverbs 31:12,15). Simple enough. You are making deposits. But let us say a word about your husband being a sinner. During this two-week period, get ready for him to do something that hurts you. For example, you have greeted him, hugged him and fixed his favorite meal, but later he angrily accuses you of moving his keys. Don't throw up your arms saying, "Oh, respecting you doesn't work. You don't appreciate me. You are as grouchy and unloving as you've always been." Remember, this is a fast from complaints. Lower your expectations. Are you expecting him to change in every area of his life because you did three honoring things? We wish we could say that wives would not approach things this way; sadly, some do. They want a perfect experience right now. Let go of that, at least for two weeks! Do this for Christ, not for your husband! You are doing this because God commands this, not because you are going to have an article written about you in a Christian magazine, "Husband Changes Into a Casa Nova When Christian Wife Does Three Nice Things."

DAY 4. When he is around, say something honoring about him in front of the children or his peers. Remember, the Bible says, "Honor all" (1 Peter 2:17). Say perhaps, "Your dad fixed the broken pipe. Without his abilities, we'd have to pay a ton of money to others." Or, "When it comes to math, few are as smart as your dad. Ask him to help you with that problem." Or, "Your dad works every day so we can have this home. He is a very hard worker." Or, "Do you know what I admired about your dad when we first dated? It was...." This kind of thing is not hard for you as a woman. You have verbal aptitudes off the charts. We are talking two, maybe three sentences, right? When a wife says, "Oh, I could never say that," she just lied! God has gifted you to communicate. You can say it, and say it quite easily. The truth is you do not want to say something honoring to a man that you feel isn't as nice to you as you want him to be. You have locked into the notion that he must earn your respect. Yes, we know you may be upset with him. Yes, we know he should be honoring you. Yet, the mature moves first. The mature wife looks beyond her husband and speaks these words because the Lord wants this. This isn't about your husband. This is about obeying God's command. Unconditional, "respectful behavior" wins even a "disobedient" husband (1 Peter 3:1,2). Or, as Peter says, "not returning...insult for insult, but giving a blessing instead" (1 Peter 3:9). You can give a verbal blessing. No sweat.

DAY 5. Squeeze his muscle and tell him he is strong (1 Corinthians 16:13). Don't make a big deal of it. Do it quickly and in passing. Don't laugh. Just do it. You're not a man. Don't try to figure this out. Your son, not your daughter, stands in front of the mirror flexing like a World Federation wrestler. Men have a protective instinct. When you comment on their strength, you are commenting on their manhood. Just as you urge your husband to tell your daughter she looks nice in her new dress because you understand her feminine feelings, so we urge you to cross over into the male arena. Your husband doesn't need to be Atlas. He just needs to feel you see him as strong to you. Go ahead. Squeeze it! He'll flex.

DAY 6. Think of something he would enjoy doing in the evening (Romans 12:10). Say, "I'd like to play a board game; when can we play?" Or, "I want to ride bikes with you; when can we ride?" Or, "I feel like watching a baseball game with you tonight. The Yankees are playing at 8:00." If he declines due to some other thing he has to do, that's fine. You sent a positive message. If he's on the couch at 8:00 to watch the game, be there! Again, if you are hurting over some unresolved issue, put aside that issue. You are fasting from complaints and pouting. (Let us insert that many of you may feel we are profiling you as temperamental and immature. We apologize. If you are not negatively reacting this way, we applaud you. You are mature and wise. But we've heard too many stories of some wives reacting just this way in the home when hurting, and we seek to serve her by countering that propensity.) As you watch the game and he says, "You have really changed. What has gotten into you?" Just say, "Thank you. I wanted to be together shoulder-to-shoulder tonight. Tell me again about that third baseman, didn't he have a run-in with the law recently?" Change the subject. Pull him out on some topic related to the activity. If you are hurting about that other issue, sit tight on it. Please do not enter that discussion. We want you to be with him to be with him, not to talk to him about your burdens. Yes, talk, but talk about positive things. Please do not think we are being parochial. The wisest of women can be too negative to her husband. This is a habit confessed to by many, and research has revealed this. So during this time, discover within yourself that you don't have to talk when you are with him. We want you to learn that you can energize him immensely by simply being with him. Don't rob yourself of this moment to make huge deposits.

DAY 7. Leave a note for him that says, "Thank you for wanting to work hard for the family. That desire and commitment makes me feel secure." Words are healing (Proverbs 16:24). Hang in there. You are halfway through. Keep an open heart toward God. Let God act on your behalf in your response to these plans. "The mind of man plans his way, but the Lord directs his steps" (Proverbs 16:9).

DAY 8. Relay a compliment about him. Reflect over the last several weeks.

Did someone say something positive and honoring to you about your husband? Build him up (1 Thessalonians 5:11). Say, "I forgot to tell you, but so and so said about you..."

DAY 9. Ask his opinion on some issue related to his expertise or interests (Philippians 2:4). If he is a political junkie, ask a political question. Look at him and listen. If he is a sports enthusiast, ask a sports question. Ask a question in an area that interests him. You are letting him know that you respect his insights.

DAY 10. Apologize (James 5:16). Think back over the last several days (or weeks) when you should not have said something. Apologize, but do it this way: "I was reflecting on something I said the other day. I said that disrespectfully. The way I said that was wrong. I am sorry. Will you forgive me?" He may have been 90% to blame. This is not done to re-open that topic. You are apologizing for your disrespectful part. If he starts justifying himself just say, "Honey, you don't have to get into that. I am apologizing for my disrespect. Will you forgive me?" When he says, "Yes," respectfully say, "Thank you," and go do some task. Again, please don't use this as an occasion to rehash the conflict. The showing of respect during this two weeks is not done for the purpose of getting him to look at his failure to love. You are showing respect in obedience to God's Word to show respect. You are doing this as a follower of Christ.

DAY 11. Ask him about his dreams and desires. "Honey, if you could do anything, what would you dream of doing? More than anything else, what would energize you?" Let him joke about sex, but say, "Apart from that, what would you most love to do, and why?" If he says, "Why do you ask?" just say, "I've heard that question before but never asked you." Also, in asking this question you are not committing yourself to help him experience that dream. This is just a fun discussion. Don't be afraid of it. He isn't going to go act on this just because you asked him about it. Since God is at work in all of us to will His good pleasure (Philippians 2:13), your husband might share things deep from his spirit. It will honor him as you listen.

DAY 12. Ask him how you can pray for him (James 5:16). We are assuming he is a believer. If he is not, try it anyway, unless he has told you not to bring up spiritual things. For instance, if he is a board member at the church, ask him, "How can I pray for you so that God will continue to use your abilities among the board members?" If he is burdened about something at work, ask, "How can I pray for you so that God will honor your good efforts?" Or, "I know our neighbor Joe has not been showing you the respect he should, how should I pray for you?"

DAY 13. Initiate sex with him (Song of Solomon 3:1; 5:6). Don't just respond; initiate. We believe you should have sex on a regular basis. If a husband or a wife is deprived, he or she can be subjected to a satanic attack. Read 1 Corinthians 7:5. When either of you deprives the other, temptation comes. A husband can feel put down for who he is when rejected sexually.

DAY 14. Say to him, "I was thinking today about all the things about you that I respect, and I want you to know that I really respect you" (Ephesians 5:33; 1 Peter 3:2). Exit the room. When he asks, if he asks, be prepared to tell him three things (Proverbs 16:23).

DAY 15. Tell us what happened! Send us your story in an email to emerson@loveandrespect.com. We'd love to hear from you!

Discussion: Report what happened with "The Respect Plan." Report the good things that happened. Stress the positive. Set your minds on that which is honorable. Talk about the honorable things that took place. Remember Philippians 4:8.

Session 18: Write a Card: Beyond Your Words of Love, Say It His Way. The Card He'll Keep!

Do you remember our discussion about how a husband is wired by God to serve and to die? That when he hears and sees respect for him something happens that motivates him to do this? Along these lines, we would like to suggest something that may come across as a bit corny. But we predict your husband will see it as anything but corny. Write a respect card, not a love card. As an example, you might try something along the lines of the following:

"Dear (term of endearment),
I was thinking of you, that you would literally die for me. That is an overwhelming thought. Thank you. With All My Respect, Signed (Your Name), the one who still admires you."

Trust us, he won't throw that card away! After one husband had heard me talk about the concept of the Respect Card he wrote the following: "I had received a 'Respect Letter'

> "An excellent wife is the crown of her husband."
> – Proverbs 12:4

(seems more appropriate than just calling it a love letter) from (my wife)... I was so amazed by this letter, I saved it...it clearly had a powerful effect on me. Not only did I save it, I read it and re-read it."

Emerson was once talking to a husband about wives writing Respect Cards and how men keep them. The man immediately opened his Bible and said, "My wife wrote me one a year ago and I keep it in my Bible!" It dawned on Emerson that a year ago he had spoken to a woman's Bible study about doing this and this man's wife had been there.

Another man wrote: "Just yesterday, (my wife) wrote me a thank you letter telling me how much she appreciated how hard I work and all that I am able to get accomplished because of my FOCUS. She's talking my language for the first time in eighteen years of marriage. All of her previous love notes were how much she loved me."

One wife had feelings of respect for her husband, but had never expressed them. One Valentine's Day she decided to write a Respect Card and told us about it: "It feels wonderful for me to get these words that I feel (but unfortunately rarely said until recently) down on paper, and I know [my husband] will cherish my Valentine's card for a long time."

Another wife reflected on the cards she had sent her husband over the years. Could it be true that he didn't keep her love cards? She wrote us the following letter on what she discovered:

"Having returned home from a Valentine Date Night at our church with Emerson as the speaker for the evening, we, as a couple, were discussing how on target he was in his understanding and explanation of the communication that happens (or doesn't happen) between husbands and wives. As his message of love and respect was so vividly communicated using practical tips and powerful illustrations, we decided to put one of them to the test. He asserted that women often give cards to their husbands full of flowery language, I love you's and illustrated with hearts and xxx's and ooo's. Often these token cards wind up in file thirteen – the trash. On the other hand, he suggested that if the wife instead wrote in a language he could understand, 'I respect you. I admire you for... I look up to you because...' that the husband would treasure such a written gesture and would save it for a lifetime. Well, we had just finished cleaning out our files from college (where we met) and the past sixteen years of marriage. (My husband) kept a file of notes and letters I'd given him over the course of eighteen years. And you know what? You betcha! All of the ones he chose to keep contained phrases of respect, honor, and admiration. He'd never been able to explain why he kept some and chucked the others, but listening to Emerson helped to put it all together! Thanks for your ministry to the body of Christ and for helping couples to crack the code. Keep up the good/God work!!"

Here's another scenario to think about. Butch was the quiet type. Excellent administrator. Barbara was sanguine. The life of the party. Sometimes she would lash out at Butch for his insensitivity. Later, she felt horrible. She would apologize. She would write little notes to him in cards. "Please forgive me. There is no one in the whole world I L.O.V.E. more than you. I love you, I love you, I love you. xoxoxoxo. Butch, I love you soooooooo much!" He said very little about these cards except when she asked, and then he would say, "Thank you." She'd find them later in his waste can. He never kept them.

As we mentioned earlier, many husbands wrote us to gush about the Respect Cards they had received. One of them wrote: "I guess if there's one fan I want in the world it would be (my wife). And this letter of hers seemed to fit the bill nicely. I was pleased that she did recognize some of my sacrifices. Not that I'm looking to be a martyr... I really think Rodney Dangerfield's 'I get no respect' routine is funny, but I don't want that to be my  epitaph. The respect-love cycle you talked about is right on the money. I didn't understand why (my wife's) letter affected me so deeply until hearing your presentation nearly two years afterwards."

Beyond your words of love, say it his way. Write a Respect Card! It's the card he'll keep! Do you want your husband to act on this verse: "Rejoice in the wife of your youth" (PRO 5:18)? A Respect Card can do it!

Discussion: Bring a copy of "The Respect Card" and share what you wrote, assuming it is appropriate to share. It is okay – in fact, it is healthy – to laugh together! Tell what your husband did or did not do, after you gave him the card.

Session 19: Focus on God for the Truth

Focus on God's truth.

Nothing is more important for you and your marriage than that you whole-heartedly understand and believe the word of God on this issue. Believe the doctrine of God about how to win a disobedient husband. The Lord spoke clearly through his servant Peter: "In the same way, you wives, be submissive to your own husbands so that even if any of them are disobedient to the word, they may be won without a word by the behavior of their wives, as they observe your chaste and respectful behavior...but let it be the hidden person of the heart, with the imperishable quality of a gentle and quiet spirit, which is precious in the sight of God" (1 Peter 3:1,2,4). How much more influence exists when a husband isn't disobedient!

> "That leaves the companion of her youth, and forgets the covenant of her God;..."
> – Proverbs 2:17

Do you believe this doctrine? Years ago a wife told Emerson she was divorcing her Christian husband, who had done nothing wrong. The wife simply wanted out. In pointing out to her that this was no biblical reason for divorcing, she said, "I'll just go down the street to another minister who will tell me what I want to hear." Emerson quoted the following verse to her: "For the time will come when they will not endure sound doctrine; but wanting to have their ears tickled, they will accumulate for themselves teachers in accordance to their own desires" (2 Timothy 4:3).

> "encourage the young women to love their husbands...being subject to their own husbands, that the word of God may not be dishonored."
> – Titus 2:4,5

The fact is that in our multi-cultural, post-modern society, little value is placed on truth. You can hear whatever you want to hear from someone, and most folks are more committed to being open-minded about all truths being equal than they are committed to finding out what God has to say on a matter and obeying that. Very few folks will encourage you to buck the cultural trend. The Person and words of Jesus Christ are not absolute to them. So the ball is inevitably and utterly in your court. It's up to you whether you genuinely want to obey what God has to say to you on this matter. It's between you and God, and the full responsibility is yours. You can find friends to help you do that, or you can find friends who will pull you away from it.

> "they are blind guides of the blind. And if a blind man guides a blind man, both will fall in a pit."
> – Matthew 15:14

So we assert as best we can what we know to be the truth, that our teaching on love and respect in Ephesians 5:33 is sound doctrine. Paul wrote, "we are no longer to be children, tossed here and there by waves, and carried about by every wind of doctrine, by the trickery of men, by craftiness in deceitful scheming" (Ephesians 4:14). God has established basic spiritual laws. When one goes against His truth, one cannot win.

> "The prophets prophesy falsely, And the priests rule on their own authority; And My people love it so! But what will you do at the end of it?"
> – Jeremiah 5:31

Did you hear the story about the warship Admiral who was contacted over radio by an enlisted Navy man? The enlisted man radioed for the Admiral to change course, saying that the Admiral was about to have a terrible collision with him. The Admiral radioed back that he was in a warship and would not change course, and besides, he was an Admiral who gave the orders. The enlisted man radioed back, instructing him to change course immediately. The Admiral angrily refused, because he was a ranking officer and leader of a huge battleship. Then the Admiral heard, "Well, Sir, I am a low-ranking midshipman, but I am overseeing the light house. Change course!" To stay the course of disrespect is a certain collision course with grief.

> "who must be silenced because they are upsetting whole families, teaching things they should not teach, for the sake of sordid gain."
> – Titus 1:11

Dear friend, please understand the vital import of what it means to accept God's teaching on this matter. Peter's words are sound doctrine on the subject of marriage! However difficult it might be to resist, we implore you not to turn to supposed teachers who will teach you things in accordance with your selfish desires. We know that unconditional respect feels unnatural! It is not in accordance with our desires. We are fallen creatures and our natural desires may lead us terribly, terribly astray. We need to hear and heed God's Word to us. Beware of how easy it is to turn to people who will readily tell you what you want to hear, who will mock what God says on this subject. We hope and pray you will let your love for God and His Word overcome that kind of temptation.

Two thousand years ago the Apostle John said, "His commandments are not burdensome" (1 John 5:3). More recently, an old country preacher exclaimed, "When God says 'No' He is saying, 'Don't hurt yourself.'" Trust that when you act on this doctrine of God – on any doctrine of God – it will bless you and help you, not hurt you. It is not a burden but a means to relieving the burden. This is sound doctrine. Turn to Jesus for strength to do the right thing. And remember His words: "Therefore everyone who hears these words of Mine, and acts upon them, may be compared to a wise man, who built his house upon the rock" (Matthew 7:24). Act on God's word! His doctrine works! You can win a disobedient husband.

The wife of an unbelieving husband wrote us:

"Dear Dr. and Mrs. Eggerichs, My husband was raised in a religious home. He hasn't attended his church since 1980 [his first wedding] but, he felt like he still had a relationship with God. I was raised in a non-Christian home, and finally gave my heart to Christ on Christmas Eve 2000 at your service you did for Trinity Church. From then, I have been 'on fire.' Soon after that I felt the need to be baptized. Whenever I talked to my husband about baptism, he would respond, 'I don't need to.' I would respond with things like, 'Yeah, but you were a baby, it didn't mean anything.' I would doubt his faith .

"The weekend that I was to be baptized, we attended your Love and Respect Conference. It wasn't until that weekend that I understood what I was doing to him.

"I prayed that Saturday afternoon, and cried while I prayed like never before. I asked the Lord's forgiveness for belittling my husband, and thanked the Lord for using you to reach me. I prayed that if that is what my husband wanted for our family then I was willing to go with it. I put it all in God's hands, and said 'it's all Yours.'

"That night, I sent my husband an e-mail [we work opposite shifts]. I told him...that I was truly sorry for making him feel like he was less of a man. I told him that I would stay off his back about it. After he read his e-mail that night, he came to me and thanked me. He didn't want to talk about it, though, and at that point it was okay! Now let me give you a little personality description here. My husband is very reserved. He is not the type of guy that is going to yell your name across the parking lot. So, what I am about to tell you came as a complete shock to me.

"We attended the Survivor Outreach at Trinity on April 8th... At the end of the Outreach, Rick Amato said a prayer, and asked anyone who wanted to accept Christ as their Savior to pray with him. After that, he had asked for those people who meant it to stand up. When my husband grabbed my hand and stood up, you could have knocked me over with a feather. Never would I have imagined in a million years that he would have taken that step. I went forward with him that night, and we have not been the same since. We have never felt this kind of love for one another. We have recently been taking the Trinity Church Discovery Class to consider membership, and that has been awesome. We read the Bible together, we pray together, and I could go on and on.

"When I pray, there are times when I thank the Lord for you and Sarah. I thank Him for working through you to open our eyes!... You are really on to something with this ministry. I just wish everyone in the world knew about it!"

Whether your husband is an unbeliever, a carnal Christian, or a godly follower, this doctrine is true and it works! God's Word does not lie. Rather, through the Apostle Peter, it reveals the foundational secret – unconditional respect – that cracks the code to a husband's spirit so that his wife might be mightily blessed.

Discussion: Share your testimony as to why you believe the Bible is the Word of God, and this respect doctrine is not a suggestion to take or leave.

Session 20: Focus on God in Prayer

Every Christian wife we've met prays to God. She prays for her husband. She looks to God for insight and tools to improve her marriage. In the first century, the wives asked the apostle Peter, "How do I win my husband? He is disobedient to the Word." Peter, as well as Paul, reveals God's answer to her burden (1 Peter 3:2). Unconditional respect. They also clearly implied that

> "With all prayer and petition pray at all times in the Spirit, and with this in view..." – Ephesians 6:18
> "...devoted to prayer..." – Romans 12:12
> "O Thou who dost hear our prayer..." – Psalm 65:2

prayer over the situation is a big part of the solution. In effect, wives are to imitate Jesus ("in the same way" - I Peter 3:11) by entrusting themselves to God who judges righteously (I Peter 2). Peter says that God is watching and hears the prayers of godly wives: "For the eyes of the Lord are upon the righteous, and His ears attend to their prayer, but the face of the Lord is against those who do evil" (1 Peter 3:12). Peter urges all to, "be of sound judgment and sober spirit for the purpose of prayer" (1 Peter 4:7).

Have you been asking God to answer your questions concerning your marriage? Are you questioning His answers? Here's a Scripture worth considering: "The Pharisee stood and was praying thus to himself, 'God, I thank Thee that I am not like other people: swindlers, unjust, adulterers, or even like this tax-gatherer. (Luke 18:11).'"

Guard against the self-righteousness that would prompt you to pray for your husband to be more loving, but not for yourself to be more respectful. Some wives have confessed to us that they believe they are better than their husbands. To them, women are the better sex. They care more, listen more, empathize more, nurture more, and love more. That is looking at male and female through pink female lenses. God designed you to love, so you will love better than your husband, or at least in the area of your strength, which is nurturance. There is truth in this. This is why God commands your husband to agape-love, and not you! If because of this you become self-righteous and react toward your husband with contempt, you may be more loving, but you are not pleasing to Jesus on this front. Read Luke 18, in which Jesus tells a story: "And He also told this parable to certain ones who trusted in themselves that they were righteous, and viewed others with contempt" (Luke 18:9). Self-righteousness and contempt are not acceptable to our Lord.

One woman accused Jesus Christ of being uncaring. She felt she knew far better than He the nature of love. We read, "But Martha was distracted with all her preparations; and she came up to Him, and said, 'Lord, do You not care that my sister has left me to do all the serving alone? Then tell her to help me'" (Luke 10:40). Can you comprehend this? Telling God He does not care. That's a bit self-righteous. Martha was serving and giving. She wanted to be understood, defended, and rescued. Her mistake was launching into accusation. She was wrong in her assessment that the incarnated God did not care.

> "Draw near to God and He will draw near to you."
> – James 4:8
> "Be gracious to us, O Lord, be gracious to us; For we are greatly filled with contempt." – Psalm 123:3

A judgmental, self-righteous outlook is such a sad thing. One wife wrote, "I am asking God to open my eyes to the many ways I disrespect my husband. I am sure there are many and I have a lot to learn...but it can only be done if I look beyond my faulty husband to my Heavenly Husband who will take care of me no matter what happens."

We invite you to pray based on the Scriptures. You need God, and God desires to be needed. We love the verse in Hebrews 4:16, "Let us therefore draw near with confidence to the throne of grace, that we may receive mercy and may find grace to help in time of need." And always be mindful of the words of our Lord Jesus, "apart from Me you can do nothing" (John 15:5).

Here is a prayer for us all when we need help with the challenge of following God's Word in our marriages:

"Father, bring to my mind ways to use respect words, not just love words. And help me avoid words of disrespect."

Colossians 4:6   **Let your speech always be with grace, seasoned, as it were, with salt, so that you may know how you should respond to each person.**

2 Samuel 6:16,20	**Michal...saw King David leaping and dancing before the Lord; and she despised him in her heart...said, "How the king of Israel distinguished himself today! He uncovered himself today in the eyes of his servants' maids as one of the foolish ones shamelessly uncovers himself!"**
Psalm 5:2	**Heed the sound of my cry for help, my King and my God, For to Thee do I pray.**

"Lord, remind me to ask myself before I do or say something, if this is going to come across respectfully or disrespectfully."

Proverbs 16:23	**The heart of the wise teaches his mouth, And adds persuasiveness to his lips.**
Ephesians 5:33	**... let the wife see to it that she respect her husband.**
Proverbs 12:4	**...she who shames him is as rottenness in his bones**.

"Spirit of God, work in me so that my look is respectful. If I am going to appeal to my husband to be more loving, help me make that appeal with a respectful tone and facial expression. Let me not be disrespectful in attitude to motivate him to be loving."

Esther 1:17	**For the queen's conduct will become known to all the women causing them to look with contempt on their husbands...**
Proverbs 19:13	**...the contentions of a wife are a constant dripping.**
Judges 14:16	**And Samson's wife wept before him and said, "You only hate me, and you do not love me..."**
Psalm 22:11	**Be not far from me, for trouble is near; For there is none to help.**

"Jesus, you know how we women love to be loved, and to receive love cards and give love cards. You've made us sentimental. But help me go beyond my words of love and write him cards of respect. He needs this like I need love."

Genesis 29:32	**now my husband will love me.**

Esther 1:20	**all women will give honor to their husbands, great and small.**
Proverbs 12:4	**An excellent wife is the crown of her husband**
1 Corinthians 11:7	**... the woman is the glory of man.**

"Lord, use my women friends to stimulate me. I need the encouragement and admonishment to trust and obey You. It is far more about me following You than anything else. Let me turn toward the godly wise in my life. Let me not be fearful of asking my husband if I have come across disrespectfully."

Romans 15:14	**... I myself also am convinced that you yourselves are ... able also to admonish one another.**
Hebrews 10:25	**...not forsaking our own assembling together, as is the habit of some, but encouraging one another....**
Psalm 28:2	**Hear the voice of my supplications when I cry to Thee for help**

"You are my loving Lord, and I choose to obey the truth of Your word. This is Your revelation to me through Paul and Peter. I believe this marriage doctrine on how to win a husband Your way."

Ephesians 5:33	**Nevertheless let each individual among you also love his own wife even as himself; and let the wife see to it that she respect her husband.**
1 Peter 3:1,2	**...you wives... even if any of them are disobedient to the word, they may be won without a word by the behavior of their wives, as they observe your... respectful behavior.**

"I thank you Lord, for the opportunity to respect my husband's desires. You have created him to work, to protect and provide, to be strong and lead, to analyze, to need me as his friend, and need me sexually. I thank You for this understanding. I will show him respect unto You. Though he fails, I will honor his desires deep within his heart."

Genesis 2:18	**Then the Lord God said, "It is not good for the man to be alone; I will make him a helper suitable for him."**
Ephesians 5:24	**But as the church is subject ("hupotasso") to Christ, so also the wives {ought to be} to their husbands in everything.**
1 Timothy 2:12	**But I do not allow a woman to teach or exercise authority over a man, but to remain quiet.**
Proverbs 19:13	**... the contentions of a wife are a constant dripping.**
1 Timothy 2:14	**being quite deceived, fell into transgression.**
Titus 2:3,4	**Older women...that they may encourage the young women to love (phileo) their husbands...**
1 Corinthians 7:5	**Stop depriving one another, except by agreement for a time that you may devote yourselves to prayer, and come together again lest Satan tempt you because of your lack of self-control.**
Psalm 69:13	**But as for me, my prayer is to Thee, O Lord, at an acceptable time... Answer me...**

"God of hope, grant to me an optimistic and patient spirit when he does not respond as quickly as I want. You know how quickly I can be hurt and lash out in anger and words of judgment."

1 Peter 3:4,5	**but let it be the hidden person of the heart, with the imperishable quality of a gentle and quiet spirit, which is precious in the sight of God. For in this way in former times the holy women also, who hoped in God..."**
Proverbs 21:19	**It is better to live in a desert land, Than with a contentious and vexing woman.**
Judges 16:15,16	**"How can you say, 'I love you,' when your heart is not with me?"... And it came about when she pressed him daily with her words and urged him, that his soul was annoyed to death.**
Proverbs 30:21,23	**... the earth quakes... it cannot bear up: Under an unloved woman...**

"More than anything else, help me do this unto Christ. Ultimately, it isn't about my husband but about me loving and revering You. This isn't about him being superior to me or about him earning respect. This isn't about me feeling respect. This is about my faith and obedience toward You."

Ephesians 5:21,22,33

and be subject to one another in the fear of Christ...Wives...as to the Lord...let the wife see to it that she respect her husband.

Malachi 1:6

"'A son honors his father, and a servant his master. Then if I am a father, where is My honor? And if I am a master, where is My respect?' says the Lord of hosts to you, O priests who despise My name. But you say, 'How have we despised Thy name?'"

Psalm 32:5

I acknowledged my sin to Thee, And my iniquity I did not hide; I said, "I will confess my transgressions to the Lord"; And Thou didst forgive the guilt of my sin.

"Lord, I close with confessing those many times I have sinned against You when I have been disrespectful toward my husband. My response is my responsibility. My husband does not cause me to be disrespectful. My husband reveals my disrespect. This is my disobedience against You and Your command. Forgive me, Lord. This isn't about me taking into account all the wrongs suffered due to his unloving manner. If I take into account these wrongs suffered, I violate the Love Chapter, 1 Corinthians 13. I am unloving! For those times I see him as the problem, I confess my sinful reaction. I want a clear conscience before You. I love you, Lord, and want to honor and respect You. In Jesus' Name, I pray."

Discussion: Though you prayed these prayers alone, pray as a group. Don't talk during this session but spend the whole time taking turns praying these prayers.

Session 21: Focus on God by Faith

Are you ready to make some resolves? Are you ready to apply God's Word? We have found that unless a person is asked to make a decision, that person will put it off. In all of our lives, there come moments when a decision must be made. Billy Graham realized that. His radio program is called "The  Hour of Decision." His magazine is called *Decision Magazine.* Think back on your life. During the wedding, the high point was when you exchanged vows saying, "I do" and "I will." Later, a moment came when you decided to have children. On a lesser scale, you decided to lose ten pounds. You decided to move nearer your aging parents. You decided to take out a loan for your children's college education. You decided to volunteer at the church. You decided to color your hair. You decided to rearrange the living room.

May we challenge you to commit to three things?

1. God's love, not my husband's love, will be the basis of my self-image.
2. My husband will be won over by my unconditional respect, not my disrespect.
3. I will become a woman of excellence by trusting God's love and acting respectfully.

You do not lack the ability. If you lack anything it is passion. So it isn't that you are unable to apply this one word, it's that you're unwilling. We are confident, however, that you are excited about moving forward. You are ready and willing. Let's go over these three commitments:

1. God's love, not my husband's love, will be the basis of my self-image.

a. I will keep myself in the love of God. This is a process and I will fail, but this is a must. The Bible says, "keep yourselves in the love of God" (Jude 1:21). This means I will regularly receive encouragement concerning God's love for me. I will read the Bible about this, as well as books and listen to tapes. I will talk with people about how to appropriate God's love in my life. I will learn how to trust God's love for me when feeling unloved by my husband.

b. Though my husband's love influences me, it will not determine who I am, and though his failure to love discourages me, it will not prevent me from being who God made me to be. This means I will control the highs and lows in my marriage. When things are depressing, I will not let myself be defeated. The Bible says, "I am well content...with distresses...with difficulties, for Christ's sake; for when I am weak, then I am strong" (2 Corinthians 12:10). When things are great, I will not let myself become overly optimistic. The Bible teaches us to have balance on both extremes: "I know how to get along with humble means, and I also know how to live in prosperity; in any and every circumstance I have learned the secret of being filled and going hungry, both of having abundance and suffering need" (Philippians 4:12). I am a woman of God, loved by God, who seeks emotional balance.

c. My self-image will rest on God's image of me. I am created in the image of God, not the image of my husband (Genesis 1:27). I have self-worth because God says I have worth to Him. Paul makes this point twice to the Corinthians: "For you have been bought with a price" (1 Corinthians 6:20), and, "You were bought with a price" (1 Corinthians 7:23). In other words, Jesus gave his life for me. That means I am worth Jesus to the Father. I will see myself as God sees me. I take that by faith, not feelings. I will do this because what I am saying is true truth in the heavenlies. This is God's image of me. He loves me so much it is as though I alone exist in this universe.

A mother sacrificed her life to save her only child, a little girl of three. When she grew up to young womanhood, she paid a visit to an aged friend of her departed mother, who possessed the only photograph of her mother. Taking the young lady to a room, she pointed to a lady's photo on the wall, and said, "That is your mother." Bursting into tears, the daughter exclaimed, "I live because she died." So, too, the Scripture says, "Who loved me, and gave Himself for me" (Galatians 2:20).

2. My husband will be won over by my unconditional respect, not my disrespect.

a. My husband can be influenced and changed for the better. The idea that he can never change is wrong. I can stimulate him to love (Hebrews 10:24). The Bible tells me a disobedient husband can be won. How much more so a good-willed husband? Though I have to let go of my selfish criteria for "love," there is a legitimate place to respectfully influence my husband to be more loving.

b. My unconditional respect is God's means for winning my husband. Though my love is important and needed, my husband is assured of my love. During conflict, he lacks assurance that I re-spect him. That is because I don't feel respect for him when he is unloving. My tendency is to react disrespectfully. This gets us on the Crazy Cycle. Without respect, he reacts without love. Without love, I react without respect. So, God calls me to put on unconditional respect in order to stop the craziness. I have been given power. I don't have to wait around for him to act. However, the means to exercise that power is unnatural to me. What is natural is to try to love my husband in ways that I want him to love me so that he'll change into a more loving man. God's Word though, takes my focus off love and puts it onto unconditional respect (Ephesians 5:33; 1 Peter 3:2).

c. I will resolve to show unconditional respect. If I do not, I will show dis-respect. This is an inescapable reality. I do not have the luxury of ignor-ing this. When I am unloved, I tend to react disrespectfully. I do so to motivate my husband to be more loving. That though, doesn't work. That is comparable to him choosing to be unloving in order to motivate me to be more respectful. Though I do not like the teaching of respect and am consumed by matters of love, I do, in fact, swim in the emotions of disre-spect. I have no right to denounce the teaching on respect as though it is foreign. That is not accurate. I know how to speak disrespectfully like the back of my hand. God is calling me to use that knowledge for the positive.

3. I will become a woman of excellence by trusting God's love and acting respectfully.

a.   I resolve to be a woman of excellence. The Bible stresses this: "An excellent wife is the crown of her husband (Proverbs 12:4). "An excellent wife, who can find? For her worth is far above jewels" (Proverbs 31:10). Or, of Ruth we read, "you are a woman of excellence" (Ruth 3:11). This Hebrew word is packed with meaning: able, capable, efficient, mighty, noble, powerful, strong, substantive, valiant, warrior, and wealthy. I believe that as I act respectfully and trust God's love, these characteristics will develop in me. I take this by faith. I step out in faith believing this.

b.   To trust God's love more than my husband's love is not easy. I can see my husband. I cannot see God. Yet if I trust my husband's love more than God's love, what will my life be like when my husband dies? Though I am to trust my husband's love, I resolve to put my primary trust in God: "Trust in the Lord with all your heart" (Proverbs 3:5). As a woman of excellence, God's love for me will be the direction of my heart: "And may the Lord direct your hearts into the love of God" (2 Thessalonians 3:5). My faith declares, "I am convinced that neither death, nor life...shall be able to separate us from the love of God, which is in Christ Jesus our Lord" (Romans 8:38, 39).

c.   To act respectfully when my husband is unloving is not easy. Yet, if I show my disrespect, it will not motivate my husband to have fond feelings of love for me. I can blame him for putting me in this situation or can see myself as able, capable, efficient, mighty, noble, powerful, strong, substantive, and valiant before God. Though my husband is to love me, and when he does, it makes respecting him easy, God's command to me to show respect is unrelated to what my husband does. I am stepping out in faith, to obey God's Word to me in Ephesians 5:33 and 1 Peter 3:2.

Discussion: Share the growth you see in your own faith. Affirm others after they give their testimony. Encourage one another. Somebody bring a cake to celebrate the victories.

Session 22: Grab A Partner

Enter into accountability with another woman. Getting a little help from friends is sensible. After many of our Love and Respect Conferences, some wives will get together and form accountability groups. This is a fantastic idea. Even if it's just two of you getting together regularly, you need a respect partner. If your best girlfriend is not knowledgeable of what you are reading and thinking, she is apt to dismiss what you say. Certain wives have been conditioned by our culture to be distressed by the idea of showing respect to a husband. The word respect comes laden with all kinds of unfavorable connotations. So unless and until your friends understand what you are beginning to understand, it will be very difficult for you to succeed in obeying God's Word in this area. That is – or it should be – a sobering thought. The Bible sternly warns, "If your...friend who is as your own soul, entices you secretly, saying, 'Let us go and serve other gods...you shall not yield to him or listen to him...'" (Deuteronomy. 13:6,8). There are some women in this culture who have bought into the idea that no husband deserves respect. Their feelings, as we have said, reinforce this. So, when this teaching on unconditional respect is revealed, they reject it. If you have such a "friend" who dismisses God's revelation, will you influence her or will she persuade you?

> "Iron sharpens iron, So one man sharpens another." – Proverbs 27:17

One spouse wrote: "I like reading your newsletter. It lifts me up. I hate to hear about people who are still struggling. I struggle every day but I win most times because it is easy to love God in times when it is not easy... I think it is about keeping the focus and wanting to change. Relationships are currently in a terrible state. So many couples who complain about what the other person is doing find an open ear from all their friends. It is easy to be a part of the crowd and sometimes tough to be the leader that will make changes in their relationship and then stand up for their spouse instead of jumping on the band wagon with the masses. Once you start to jump on the band wagon, even if some of the statements are not completely true, the statements transform into reasons not to show love or respect. So any person or couple must first want to change and then pray for the strength to hold true to the change."

> "Oil and perfume make the heart glad, so a man's counsel is sweet to his friend ."
> – Proverbs 27:9

Because unconditional respect is such a foreign concept, many women have decided to meet together to encourage each other. Obeying God's Word in this culture at this time in our history is not easy! One wife wrote, "The challenge now is to not drift back into old habits. Four of us women have purposed to meet once a month for accountability and review – once we put the word out I'm sure more will join us."

Find a Mentor

An older woman, someone who can serve as a mentor, can be of inestimable value to you. In Titus 2:3,4 we read, "Older women...are to...encourage the young women to love (phileo) their husbands..." A woman who has weathered the storms of a long marital relationship can provide amazing support and encouragement. She can encourage a younger wife to be friendly (phileo) and respectful in the home, even when serious tension exists. An older woman who is mature in Christ will have the ability to see things through a man's blue lenses in a way that you might not be able to. Do you have such a wise woman in your life?

When isolated with your own feelings, misinterpretations and misunderstandings can result. For example, a husband can withdraw into silence because he is seeking to do the honorable thing, rather than to respond in anger and verbal abuse. But a wife may see this as unloving on his part. He may feel you are provoking him, since if a male friend talked to him this way it would be considered provocation. In order to prevent a fight he clams up. This can be honorable to him. At the same time, you can come at him to talk because you feel this is the loving thing to do. But you are scolding him, even pointing a finger at him. He feels dishonored, which isn't your intent either. You are trying to do the loving thing by resolving the matter! An older, godly woman has learned a few things and can reassure your heart that it isn't what you think. She can encourage you and prevent you from returning to the worst habits of your old self.

Each wife should ask herself what the odds are that she will be able to act on this word from God if she has "friends" who oppose it outright. If she is frank with herself, she will recognize that the odds are probably insurmountable. People – women especially – are relational beings, who need others to encourage them to do the right thing, to buoy them up. As you read this message on motivating your man God's way, you will be encouraged. But afterward, amidst

> "He who separates himself seeks his own desire, he quarrels against all sound wisdom." – Proverbs 18:1

hostility to the ideas – or simply incomprehension – it will get tough to stay hot on the idea. When a hot coal is removed from the fire and set aside by itself, it soon burns out. But kept with the other coals, it burns and burns. Don't isolate yourself but find kindred spirits who will keep you fired up. In a woman's world, her friends can be more detrimental – or more helpful – than she realizes. One of the hardest decisions a woman may need to make is to find a new friend who wants the same for her marriage. Once that is in place however, serious progress is about to be made. There is nothing more important, so think about this and take the steps you need to take. God's Word doesn't lie, and you won't regret your decision.

Discussion: Share with the others why you need them in this "Respect Accountability" group. Tell when and why you were encouraged by another in the group. Seek to bless someone in the group.

Session 23. Understand What Empowers You

What do you want? There are some humanists who put some Christians to shame. We have the Holy Spirit within us, yet they commit themselves to self-help resources, and many do wonderfully. A small effort consistently applied can produce a big difference. If that happens with people "strangers to the covenants of promise, having no hope and without God in the world" (Ephesians 2:12), what might you do with Christ who is in you (Colossians 1:27)? You have God's help and can depend on Him. Having said that, most of the passages we have been studying are not promises but commands and principles. In other words, God is declaring that we can do what He instructs us to do. We know you want your marriage to work. We believe as you act on what you want, which is acting in obedience to the command of God, good things will happen.

We know what you want. You want to be loved for who you are. Is there anything more fulfilling? But what will you do to create an environment that ignites the feelings of love in the marriage? If you see your husband as totally responsible to initiate it, and you then are to respond, then when he fails to initiate, you are stuck. You are powerless. However, Scripture does not describe you as a passive weakling. You are no helpless and hopeless victim. Peter did not see you as powerless but that you could win your husband, even without a word (1 Peter 3:1,2). Will you give us permission to challenge you? You can do far more than you think. If there is a gap between where you want to be and where you are in your marriage, God is inviting you to close the gap! You have the ability; you have Him. You have an advantage over the humanist. You can pray as well. Peter was clear about that (1 Peter 3:12; 4:7). God has provided a great deal of inner strength. When the humanist only has herself and she makes great strides, can you do less?

Certainly you have the power to be disrespectful, and some of you are exercising that power! We know though, that you will not get what you want if you express this disrespect. It is a law of romance. Just as an unloving husband does not motivate a wife to show respect, so too a disrespectful wife does not motivate a husband to show love.

God wants for you what you want for yourself: the feeling that love exists in the marriage. His Word and way empower you as a wife. You become powerful when you use respectful talk and actions. We request that you keep asking and answering the following questions with your accountability friend:

"Am I focused on my strengths in showing respect?" Respectful behavior is a strength God has given to you as a wife. He wouldn't command this if you were incapable. Use it. You are not losing power, but gaining power. As husbands are negatively vulnerable to disrespect, those very husbands are positively vulnerable to respect. As a husband shuts down in the face of disrespect, so a husband blossoms around respect. Don't underestimate your capability in this area. In claiming this is a foreign language, please acknowledge that you have the aptitude to learn new languages. You have the competencies to act and speak with dignity.

"Am I looking for the possibilities before me?" Look for the opportunities to display a respectful attitude. The woman who closes her eyes to the numerous ways of penetrating the heart of her husband with respect loses power. The wife who keeps looking and exploring for new ways sees new avenues. If a husband isn't touched by respect talk, show respect in a way that does affect him. If you like cards and he doesn't, don't write a card. Look for a new possibility. If the house is always unclean and he feels disrespected because of it – due to repeated requests to clean it – then turn this problem into a gift from God as His means to soften your husband's spirit. An exercise that enables you to see the possibilities, is to mentally step into the future. Envision the relationship with your husband. Envision the opportunities that might arise. Remember, God can provide those opportunities. The Lord has been in the future already. He is inviting you into tomorrow, not to worry, but to respond to His initiatives. Get ready!

"Am I acting as if I am already a loving and respectful wife?" If humanists can claim "acting as if" works, how much more a believer in Jesus Christ. Another way of saying this is "obey God in faith." A godly wise wife says to herself, "The Lord calls me to be friendly and respectful. Because I don't always feel like doing this, I must step out in faith and obey God." Friends, the Bible talks about clothing oneself with various virtues. We put it on. Put on respect. Act as if you are a woman of dignity and respect. This is what a mature person does. She does what is right even though she doesn't feel like doing it. Some attitudes only change after we act. If we wait to act until our attitudes change, we'll never get around to obeying and trusting God. The power of "acting as if" not only impacts a husband, it touches God's heart.

"Am I acknowledging what I am doing right?" Let the positive and the successes bolster you. This does not mean you should deny personal failures, but that you set your mind on the good. This is a biblical teaching. The human heart can lean toward the negative, which does not reflect the whole picture. For instance, when you got four A's and one D+, did you get excited by the A's or break out in a sweat over the D+? Many fixate on the poor grade. So too, in marriage. If you zero in on your disrespectful reactions, you'll get depressed and feel defeated. The truth is, you are making impact with new ways of showing respect. Keep focusing on what you are doing right. Be grateful for what has transpired that is encouraging to you. It is not a psychological trick. If a person is obsessed with the problem, the problem is certain to get worse.

"Am I willing to practice until I form good habits?" Eventually, this can be far easier than you think. Initially, repetition is exhausting. It takes work. It is like knitting. At first everything is awkward for the novice, but watch that same lady in a year as her fingers move like lightening with the needles and yarn. The same is true with learning to type, to follow a new recipe, or to drive a stick shift. Eventually, we don't even think about these things.

"Am I re-framing what is happening?" When your husband reacts in an unloving way, he may be feeling disrespected. He isn't trying to be an unloving person. In fact, he may be doing the honorable thing by going silent and withdrawing. His blood pressure and heart rate is skyrocketing during a fight. He knows if he stays engaged, he might say or do something that could wound your heart. So, he retreats. As a woman, you cannot imagine that such a discussion would be viewed this way. Instead, you feel he is being an unloving husband. You may feel a measure of hostility toward him for repeatedly reacting this way. Re-framing means interpreting your husband as good-willed. Yes, he is hurting you and even offending you, but it isn't as unloving as you feel it to be. He is not a woman. He doesn't have a need to engage in conversation and release emotions. He prefers to drop it and move on. Is he wrong? Is he unloving? Re-framing allows you to give him the benefit of the doubt and prevents you from over personalizing situations.

"Am I strategizing?" Respectful behavior won't happen by accident. Intentionality is important. Planning is important. When it comes to your children, you are anticipating what you will do and by when. You have an inborn instinct to do this. You can see what to do and how to do it. Even when it comes to showing love to your husband, there is a built-in magnetic pull. However showing unconditional respect is unnatural. There is no compelling feeling to do this. Thus, you'll need to strategize with deliberation. When you wake up in the morning you'll need to give thought to this. For instance, if he has a major presentation at work today, plan on engaging him that evening. Go beyond asking, "How was your presentation?" If he says, "Fine" don't say, "Oh, that's nice, dear." Draw him out. Be a reporter. One of the reasons husbands are quiet is that what consumes them during the day is unimportant to the wives. Remember, Adam was created to work in the Garden. Eve wasn't created yet. Therefore, one strategy is to energize your husband by actively showing interest in his "field." Do you retort, "Work? He's supposed to work. I work too, so I could care less about strategizing to affirm him. He needs to affirm me." True, but if you're more mature, you move first. Don't underestimate what a little comment can do to the spirit of your husband. To ignore this is like him never talking to you about the children. A little thought and effort pays big dividends. What would you feel if your husband said, "I appreciate your mothering. The way you responded to Kelly just then was so wise." You know how precious that comment would be; so strategize on finding those areas that energize him as a male. Those areas are there and often untapped because they seem irrelevant to a wife.

"Am I showing movement?" Keep moving forward. Taking action, no matter how small, can be significant. There is a profound truth in the expression, "small change, big difference." Don't downplay doing something little each day. If your husband is good-willed and you greet him at the door with a smile for fifteen seconds, it can set the tone for the whole evening. If you haven't done that for months, it can be good for a week! Little deposit, gigantic dividend! As you move forward with some action, you can only control the process, you cannot control the outcome in your husband. You cannot do what you cannot do. Do what you can, and keep moving! Remember, you are going to be doing and saying something anyway, why not be positive and respectful? Instead of saying, "Why are you home so early?" Say, "It's good to see you home early!" You're talking anyway, why not move in the direction of respect? Again, this is done to touch the heart of your Lord and Savior. This isn't about your husband deserving this.

"Am I receiving strength from supportive friends?" You need people to stand with you in this venture, not cynically against you. Who is in your life who can give you a standing ovation when you do something respectful unto Christ? Who will be your advocate? Who will you request to ask you, "What will you do by when, and how will you know if it is done?" God's Word indicates you need an older woman in your life to encourage you. Do you have such a godly wise person? Is there someone who can keep asking, "What if you tried this?" Oh, the surge of encouragement that can come with a good word from such a precious, dignified woman.

Reflection and Discussion:

As you sit alone, jot down some thoughts as you consider each question. Share your thoughts with the group. Am I focused on my strengths? Am I looking for the possibilities before me? Am I acting as if things are very positive? Am I acknowledging what I am doing right? Am I willing to practice until I form good habits? Am I re-framing what is happening so that I see the good? Am I strategizing to move things forward positively? Am I moving forward positively?

Session 24. You Can Make A Request of Your Husband

Do you want your husband to engage the love side of the Love and Respect Connection? Do you want him to understand the Crazy Cycle from your side: without love you react without respect? Do you want him to decode what is going on deep in your heart, that you are not trying to be disrespectful but that you need his love?

What about the Energizing Cycle: his love motivates your respect? Do you want him to apply the love side of the equation, making the respect dimension easier for you? Do you want him to learn to love you in better ways so you can be more energized to love and respect?

We believe if you have done many of these assignments with your husband, you have a husband who will respond to your request to engage the Love and Respect message. We have confidence in this message, and confidence in you to make this request. You can ask him to watch the Love and Respect Marriage Conference on video, or listen to the audio portion of the conference (go to the E-store at www.loveandrespect.com). We want him to understand himself and you. That you have applied these insights has touched his heart. If we may say it this way, you have won the right to be heard. You can make an appeal to him to join a small group of husbands and wives who are focusing on enriching their marriages. We believe he'll gladly respond. He has tasted something that he likes. You have made important deposits in his heart.

In the Love and Respect Marriage Conference, we define what love is to a wife. The longing of a woman's heart is to C.O.U.P.L.E: she longs for his closeness, openness, understanding, peacemaking, loyalty and esteem. This is how a wife spells love. To her, these acts of love make a marriage: talking face to face, not remaining secretly mad, empathizing with each other, saying I'm sorry and seeking forgiveness, being completely committed to each other, and treasuring each other above all others. These are things she does naturally, and yearns for him to do more than he does. Your husband will learn the power of each of these concepts. In fact, he will discover ways to motivate you to want to show more respect to him by loving you in meaningful ways! Such a deal! Go ahead, ask him! After twenty-four weeks of doing these assignments he is apt to say, "Where can I sign up?"

Conclusion

We want for you to experience God's success in motivating your man His way.

Our old country preacher would now say, "I'm goin' to tell ya' what I just told ya'!".

Focus on what you can do. Respect is not a dirty word, so use it! Before you act, ask yourself the respect question. It's not what you say, but how you say it. Relax, you'll get there.

Focus on your husband's desires: his desire to work and achieve in his field, to protect and provide, and even die for you, to be strong, to lead and make decisions, to analyze and counsel, for a shoulder-to-shoulder friendship, and for sexual intimacy.

Plan your respect, and respect your plan!

Write a respect card: Beyond Your Words of Love, Say It His Way!

Let God have the last word. When all else fails, pray! When all else succeeds, pray! It's not about believing in your husband, but believing in God.

Grab a partner.

And, understand what empowers you.

Does this seem like too much? Compared to all that has been written on love, we think it is long overdue. Regardless, this is God's Word to wives (Ephesians 5:33b; 1 Peter 3:2). The writer of Hebrews penned, "let us consider how to stimulate one another to love" (10:24). We have considered how to motivate your husband. We believe this is God's way, and His way works!

Referenced publications:

Driscoll, Richard. 1998. *The Stronger Sex: Understanding and Resolving the Power Struggle Between Men and Women.* Roseville, CA: Prima Publishing.

Gilder, George. 1986. *Men and Marriage.* Gratna, La: Pelican Publishing Company, Inc.

Gottman, John, and Silver, Nan. 1994. *Why Marriages Succeed or Fail: And How You Can Make Yours Last.* New York: Simon & Schuster Publishers.

Goldberg, Steven. 1973. *The Inevitability of Patriarchy: Why the Biological Difference Between Men and Women Always Produces Male Domination.* New York: William Morrow & Company, Inc.

Sanoff, Alvin, "The Anatomy of Shame," U.S. News & World Report, March 9, 1992 p.56.

Tannen, Deborah. 1990. *You Just Don't Understand: Women and Men in Conversation.* New York: William Morrow, Ballantine.

Tannen, Deborah. 1994. *Gender and Discourse.* NY & Oxford: Oxford University Press.

Tannen, Deborah. 1995. *Talking from 9 to 5.* New York: Avon Books.